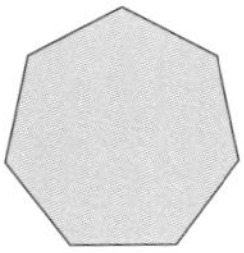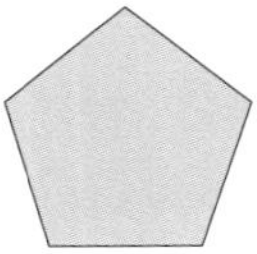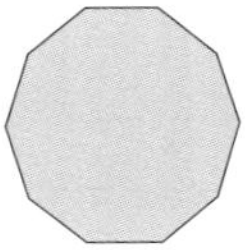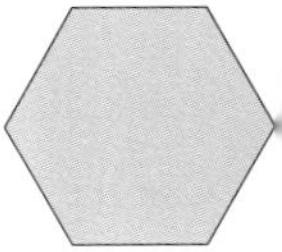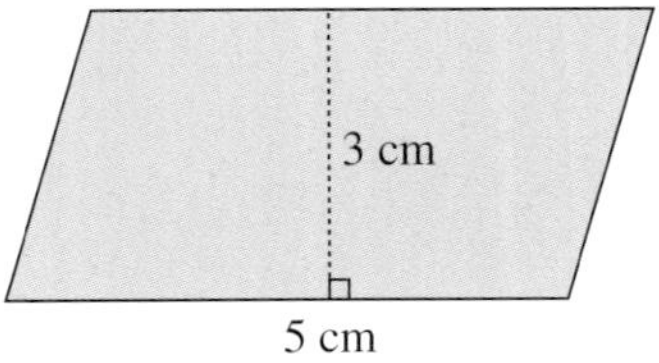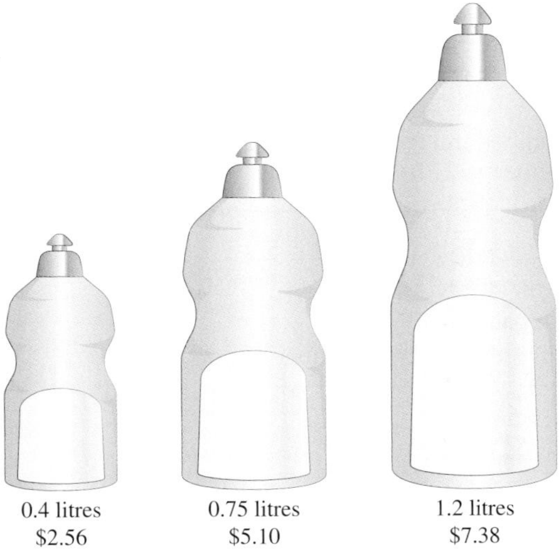

12C The *n*th term

Example

Find the nth term for the sequence 7, 8, 9, 10, 11, ...

First term is	$1+6$
Second term is	$2+6$
Third term is	$3+6$
Fourth term is	$4+6$
Fifth term is	$5+6$
nth term is	$n+6$

1 The position-to-term rule for a sequence is $n+4$.

a Find the 20th term.

b Find the 100th term.

2 The position-to-term rule for a sequence is $n-7$.

a Find the 10th term.

b Find the 50th term.

3 The position-to-term rule for a sequence is $4n$.

a Find the 40th term.

b One term has value 76. Which term is it?

4 Find the nth term of each of these sequences.

a 2, 3, 4, 5, 6, …

b 7, 8, 9, 10, 11, …

c 5, 6, 7, 8, 9, …

d $^{-}3, ^{-}2, ^{-}1, 0, 1$, …

e 4, 8, 12, 16, 20, …

f 6, 12, 18, 24, 30, …

g $^{-}2, ^{-}4, ^{-}6, ^{-}8, ^{-}10$, ...

h $^{-}7, ^{-}14, ^{-}21, ^{-}28, ^{-}35$, …

5 The nth term of a sequence is $n-5$.
How many negative terms are there in the sequence?

6 The position-to-term rule for a sequence is $7-3n$.
Write down the first five terms of this sequence.

7 The position-to-term rule for a sequence is $5n-2$.

a Find the 40th term.

b One term has value 83. Which term is it?

12E Graphs of linear functions

Example

Draw the graph of $y = x - 1$.

First make a table of values.

x	0	1	2	3
y	$^-1$	0	1	2

Then plot the points on a pair of axes.

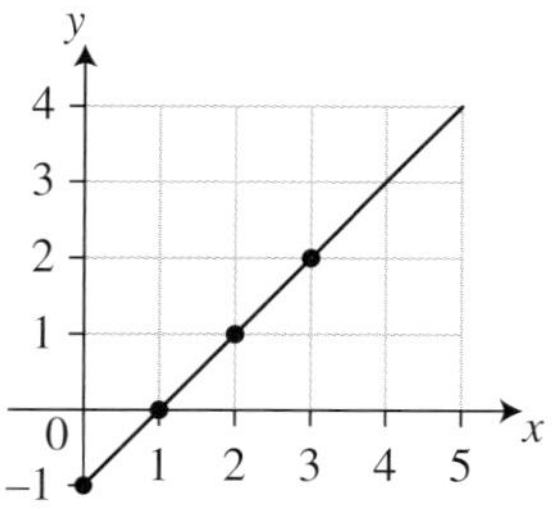

1 Copy and complete the table for $y = 2x$.
Draw the graph of $y = 2x$, choosing suitable axes.

x	0	1	2	3
y				

2 Copy and complete the table for $y = x + 1$.
Draw the graph of $y = x + 1$, choosing suitable axes.

x	0	2	4	6
y				

3 Copy and complete the table for $y = x - 2$.
Draw the graph of $y = x - 2$, choosing suitable axes.

x	0	2	4	6
y				

4 One of these points does not lie on the line $y = x + 4$. Which one is it?

($^-3$, 1) (10, 6) ($^-2$, 2) (0, 4)

5 Copy and complete the table for $y = 2x + 3$.
Draw the graph of $y = 2x + 3$, choosing suitable axes.

x	0	1	2	3
y				

6 Copy and complete these coordinate pairs for $y = 3x + 2$.

(4, □) (2, □) (0, □) (3, □)

7 Copy and complete these coordinate pairs for $y = \frac{1}{2}x - 2$.

(4, □) (10, □) (0, □) ($^-4$, □)

8 Which of these points does not lie on the line $y = 4x - 5$?

(2, 3) (0, $^-1$) (4, 11) (7, 23)

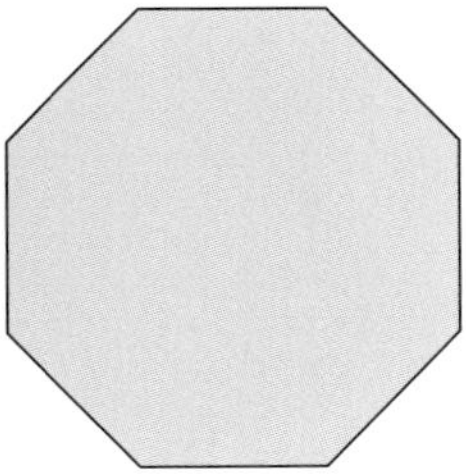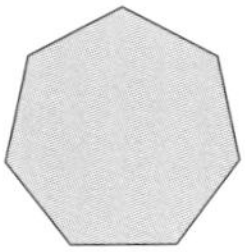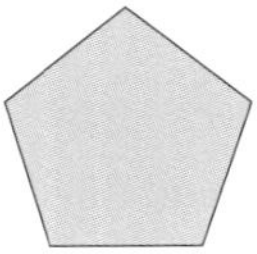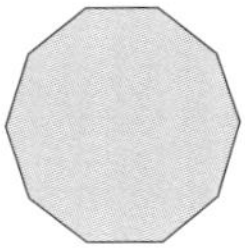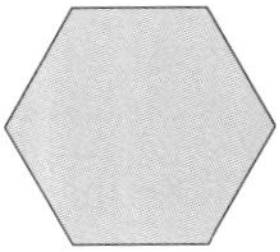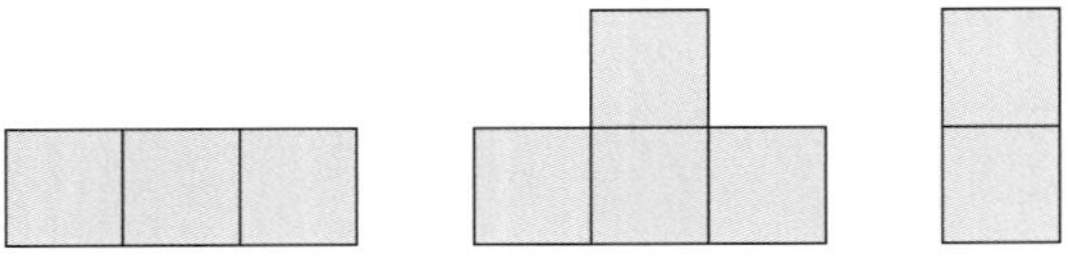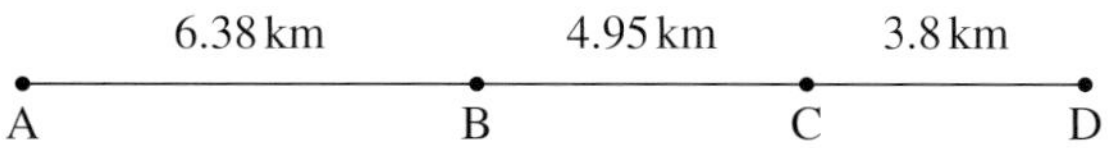

Find the distance between A and D.

Work out:

a 38.4 – 12　　**b** 9.2 – 2.8　　**c** 7 – 0.6

d 15 – 2.3　　**e** 15.3 – 6.7　　**f** 4.7 – 2.08

g 21 – 0.39　　**h** 12.68 – 4.004　　**i** 7.8 – 5.68

j 80 – 8.47　　**k** 17.3 – 6.48　　**l** 20.3 – 5.998

Find the odd one out.

5.249 – 3.184	18.605 – 15.64	3.631 – 1.566

0 Raju bought a book for \$9.35 and a pack of pens for \$7.89.
He paid with a \$20 bill.
How much change did he receive?

1 Helen and Anya took part in a long jump competition.
Helen jumped 6.45 metres and Anya jumped 5.87 metres.
How much further did Helen jump than Anya?

2 **a** By rounding each number to the nearest integer, estimate the answers to these calculations.

i $^{-}4.28 + 6.57$　　**ii** $^{-}2.77 - {^{-}3.8}$　　**iii** $^{-}1.72 - 3.98 - {^{-}1.342}$

b Now work out the exact answers and compare them to your estimates.

3 Find the missing numbers.

a
$$\begin{array}{r} 9.\square 3 \\ -\ \square.45 \\ \hline 6.88 \\ \hline \end{array}$$

b
$$\begin{array}{r} \square.4\square \\ -\ 5.\square 2 \\ \hline 2.74 \\ \hline \end{array}$$

c
$$\begin{array}{r} 4.29\square \\ -\ \square.6\square 7 \\ \hline 1.\square 46 \\ \hline \end{array}$$

4 Work out:

a $12.6 + {^{-}6.35}$　　**b** $5.8 - {^{-}4.88}$

c $^{-}12.6 + 7.21$　　**d** $5.2 + {^{-}8.9}$

e $8.4 - 10.2 + 9.65$　　**f** $^{-}8.9 + 3.3 + 5.07$

g $^{-}4.9 + 8.14 + {^{-}2.65}$　　**h** $^{-}5.8 + {^{-}5.8} - {^{-}5.8}$

12C The *n*th term

Example

Find the nth term for the sequence 7, 8, 9, 10, 11, ...

First term is	$1 + 6$
Second term is	$2 + 6$
Third term is	$3 + 6$
Fourth term is	$4 + 6$
Fifth term is	$5 + 6$
nth term is	$n + 6$

1 The position-to-term rule for a sequence is $n + 4$.

a Find the 20th term.

b Find the 100th term.

2 The position-to-term rule for a sequence is $n - 7$.

a Find the 10th term.

b Find the 50th term.

3 The position-to-term rule for a sequence is $4n$.

a Find the 40th term.

b One term has value 76. Which term is it?

4 Find the nth term of each of these sequences.

a 2, 3, 4, 5, 6, …

b 7, 8, 9, 10, 11, …

c 5, 6, 7, 8, 9, …

d $^-3, ^-2, ^-1, 0, 1$, …

e 4, 8, 12, 16, 20, …

f 6, 12, 18, 24, 30, …

g $^-2, ^-4, ^-6, ^-8, ^-10$, ...

h $^-7, ^-14, ^-21, ^-28, ^-35$, …

5 The nth term of a sequence is $n - 5$.
How many negative terms are there in the sequence?

6 The position-to-term rule for a sequence is $7 - 3n$.
Write down the first five terms of this sequence.

7 The position-to-term rule for a sequence is $5n - 2$.

a Find the 40th term.

b One term has value 83. Which term is it?

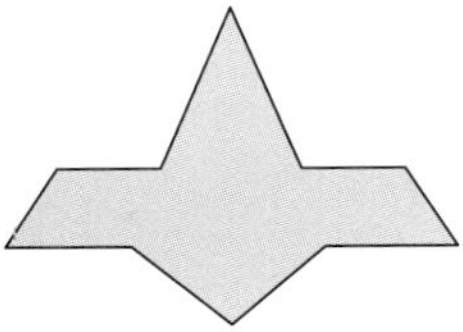

6

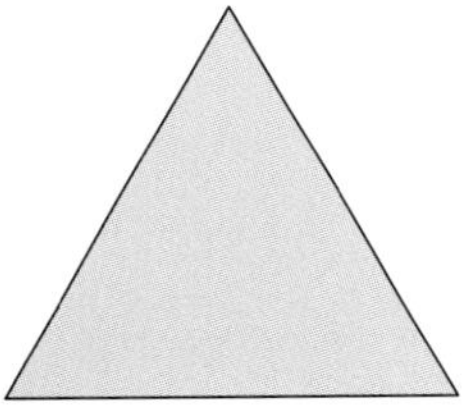

8

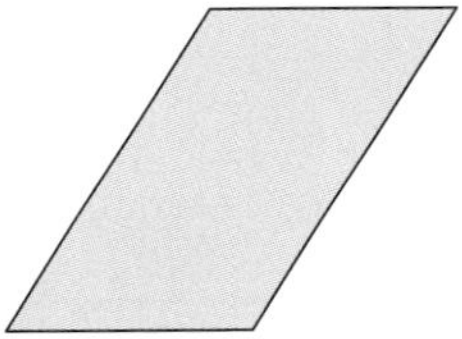

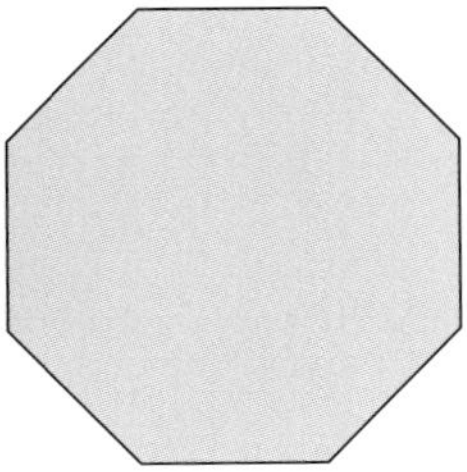

10

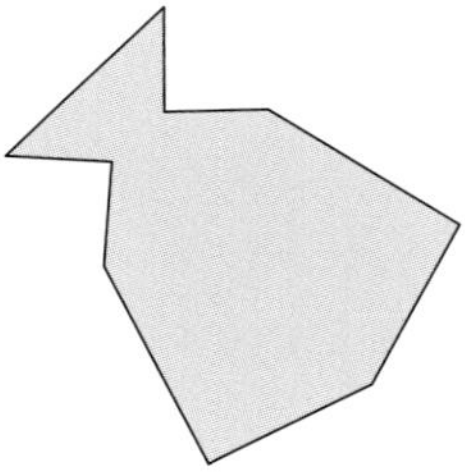

11

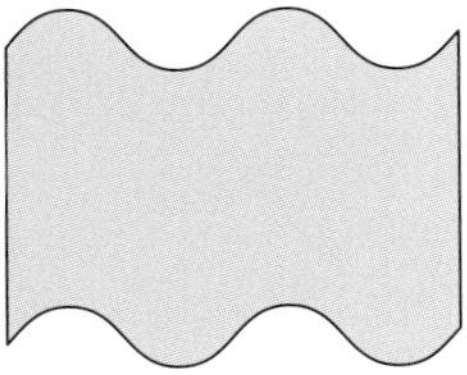

12

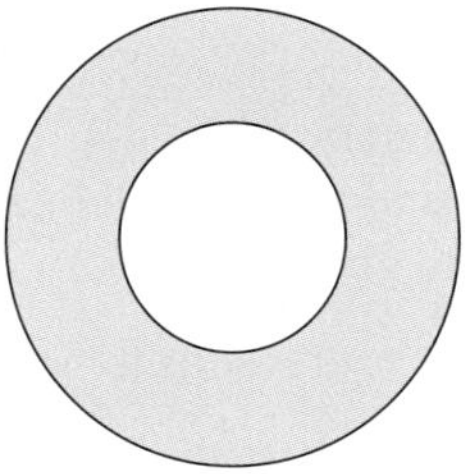

d

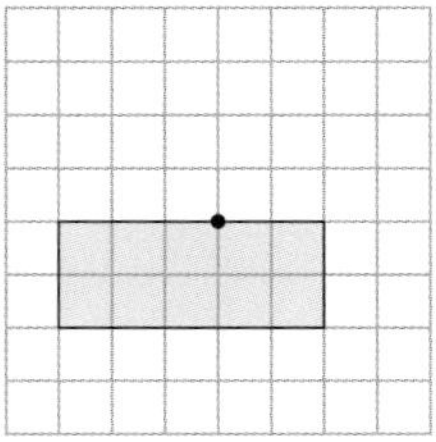

180°

e

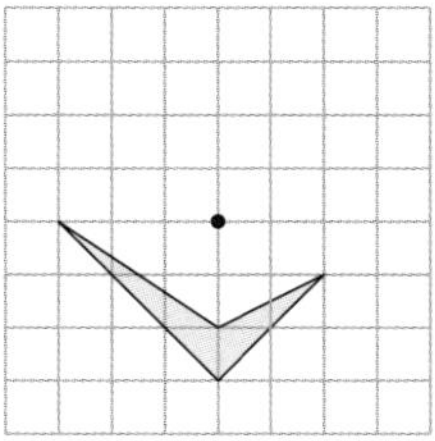

180°

f

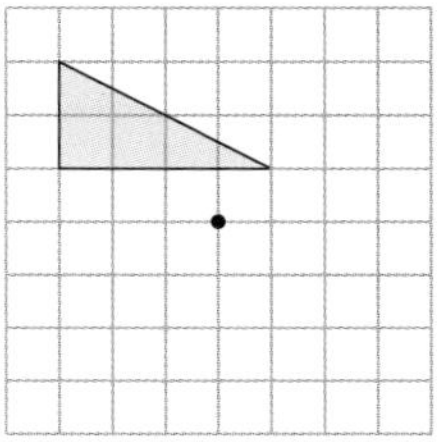

90° clockwise

g

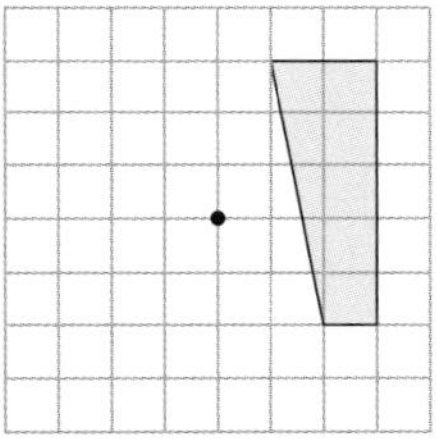

180°

h

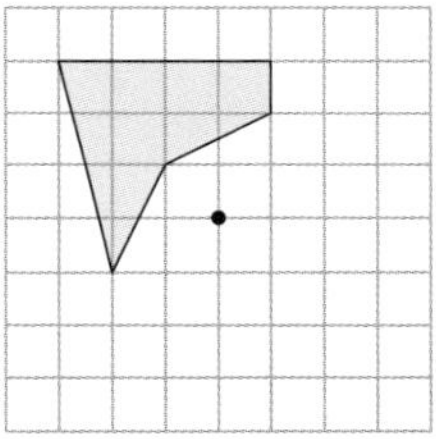

270° clockwise

i

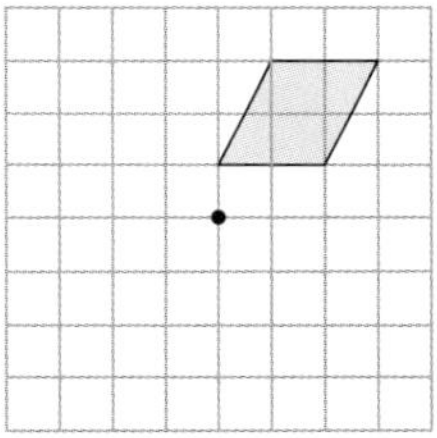

270° anticlockwise

Draw triangle ABC with vertices at (1, 0), (1, 3) and (3, 0).
Rotate triangle ABC 90° anticlockwise about the point (0, $^-1$).

Describe the rotation that maps shape A onto shape B.

a

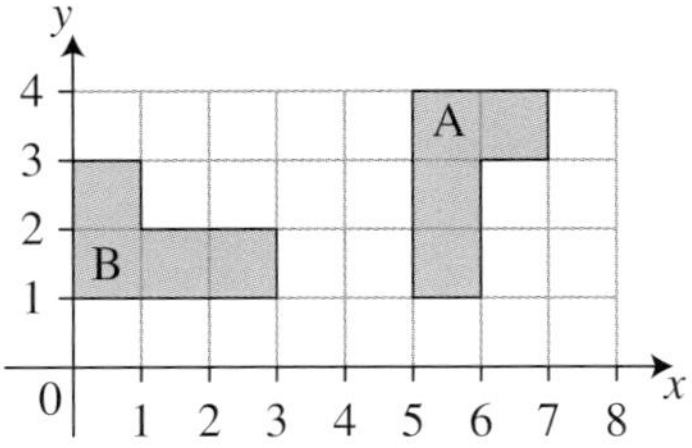

b

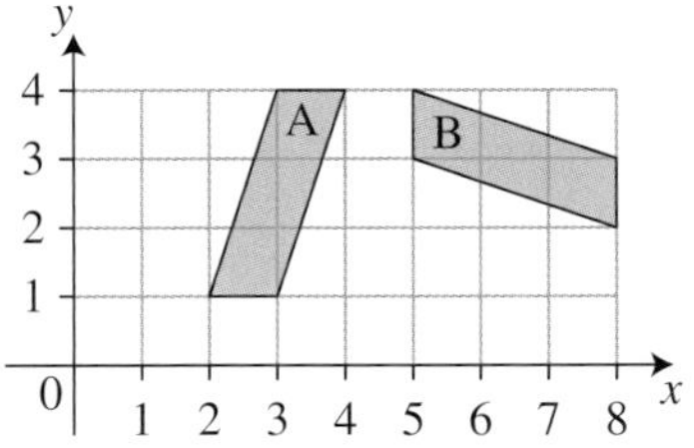

a The points (4, 0), (0, 5), (4, 2) and ($^-3$, 4) are each rotated 90° anticlockwise about the origin.

i Copy and complete the table.

Point	(4, 0)	(0, 5)	(4, 2)	($^-3$, 4)
Image	(0, 4)			

ii Describe in words a rule for writing down the image of any point after a rotation of 90° anticlockwise about the origin.

b Find a rule for writing down the image of a point after a rotation of 180° about the origin.

c Find a rule for writing down the image of a point after a rotation of 90° clockwise about the origin.

2F Expanding brackets

Example

Expand the brackets: **a** $5(2x+4)$ **b** $^-3(2x-7)$

a $5(2x+4) = 10x+20$

b $^-3(2x-7) = {}^-6x+21$

1 Expand the brackets.

a $3(x+2)$ **b** $4(y-5)$ **c** $5(8+a)$

d $6(3-p)$ **e** $2(x+y)$ **f** $3(a-b)$

g $8(m-n)$ **h** $7(p+q)$ **i** $6(2x+1)$

j $5(3y-2)$ **k** $4(6-5y)$ **l** $2(3v-4)$

m $3(2x+3y)$ **n** $4(6x-5y)$ **o** $9(4a+5b)$

p $8(3p-4q)$ **q** $^-2(x+2)$ **r** $^-4(y-1)$

s $^-3(4y+7)$ **t** $^-2(6-5y)$

2 Expand the brackets.

a $4(2a+3b-5)$ **b** $3(5x-2y+z)$ **c** $6(1+2x+3y)$

d $2(5p-3+2q)$ **e** $7(3f+2g-5h)$ **f** $10(x-2y+3z)$

g $^-3(2x+y-4)$ **h** $^-2(a-3b+7)$ **i** $^-7(3p-q+4r)$

3 Expand the brackets.

a $\frac{1}{2}(4x+6)$ **b** $\frac{1}{2}(8y-10)$ **c** $\frac{1}{3}(6x-9)$

d $\frac{1}{5}(20x-15)$ **e** $\frac{1}{4}(28x+4)$ **f** $\frac{1}{8}(16-40x)$

4 Copy and complete:

a $3(2x+\square) = 6x+15$ **b** $4(3y-\square) = 12y-8$

c $8(6x-\square) = 48x-56$ **d** $5(\square-2y) = 25-10y$

e $6(\square x+3) = 12x+18$ **f** $\square(7x+2) = 28x+8$

g $\square(5y-4) = {}^-15y+12$ **h** $^-8(\square x+5) = {}^-16x-40$

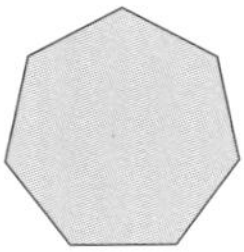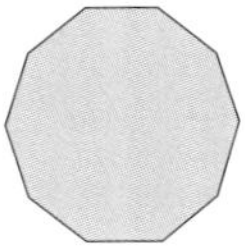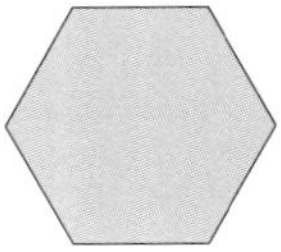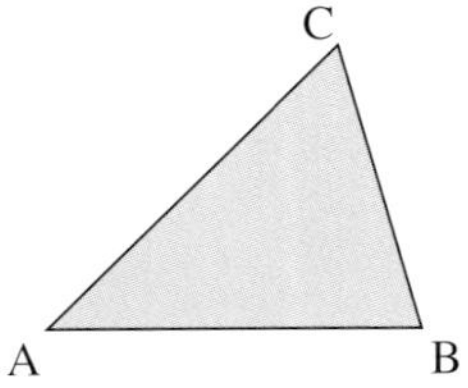

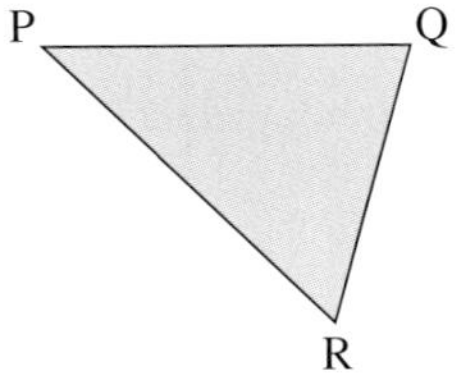

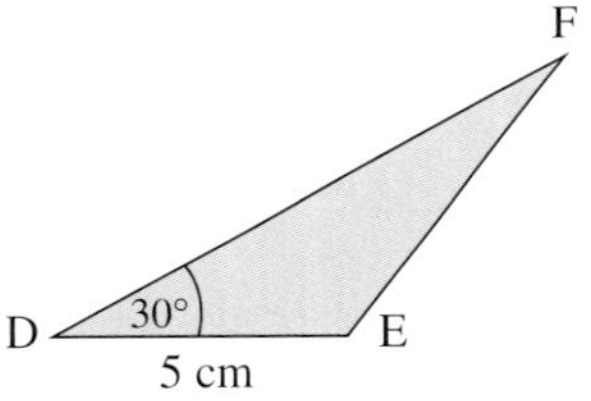

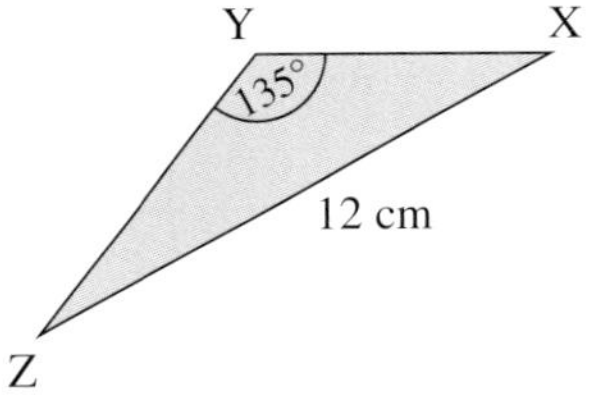

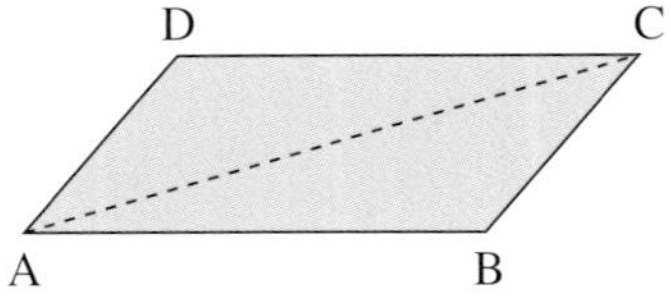

5A Units of area

Example

Convert $6\,\text{m}^2$ to square centimetres.

$1\,\text{m}^2 = 100 \times 100\,\text{cm}^2 = 10\,000\,\text{cm}^2$

So, $6\,\text{m}^2 = 6 \times 10\,000\,\text{cm}^2 = 60\,000\,\text{cm}^2$

1 Convert these measurements to square millimetres.

a $5\,\text{cm}^2$ **b** $28\,\text{cm}^2$ **c** $4.7\,\text{cm}^2$ **d** $6.34\,\text{cm}^2$

2 Convert these measurements to square centimetres.

a $700\,\text{mm}^2$ **b** $90\,\text{mm}^2$ **c** $274\,\text{mm}^2$ **d** $6273\,\text{mm}^2$

3 **a** Find the area of this rectangle in cm^2.

b Write down the area of the rectangle in mm^2.

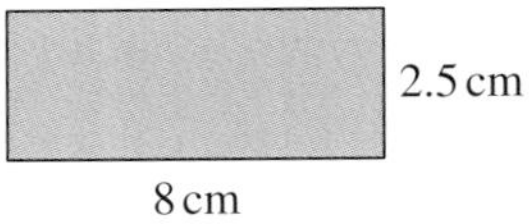

4 Convert these measurements to cm^2.

a $2\,\text{m}^2$ **b** $8\,\text{m}^2$ **c** $5.8\,\text{m}^2$ **d** $0.4\,\text{m}^2$

5 Convert these measurements to mm^2.

a $4\,\text{m}^2$ **b** $7\,\text{m}^2$ **c** $3.9\,\text{m}^2$ **d** $0.06\,\text{m}^2$

6 Convert these areas to cm^2.

a $3600\,\text{mm}^2$ **b** $3.5\,\text{m}^2$ **c** $0.8\,\text{km}^2$

7 Copy and complete.

a $0.09\,\text{km}^2 = \square\,\text{m}^2$ **b** $71\,000\,000\,\text{m}^2 = \square\,\text{km}^2$

c $0.077\,\text{km}^2 = \square\,\text{mm}^2$ **d** $500\,000\,\text{mm}^2 = \square\,\text{m}^2$

8 Convert these area measurements to hectares.

a $70\,000\,\text{m}^2$ **b** $520\,000\,\text{m}^2$ **c** $5000\,\text{m}^2$ **d** $300\,\text{m}^2$

9 This diagram shows a plot of land.

Find its area, giving your answer in hectares.

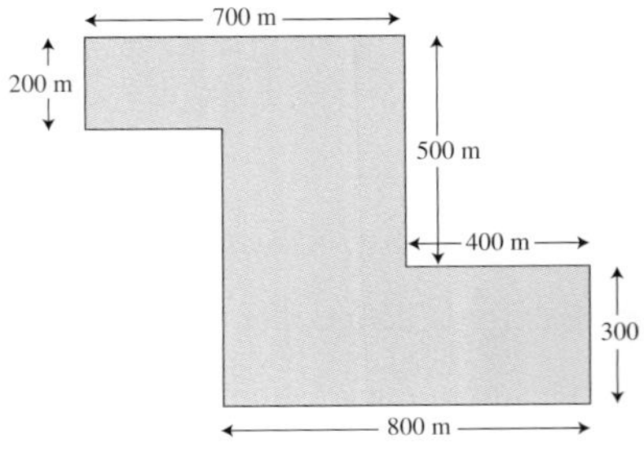

12C The *n*th term

Example

Find the nth term for the sequence 7, 8, 9, 10, 11, ...

First term is	$1 + 6$
Second term is	$2 + 6$
Third term is	$3 + 6$
Fourth term is	$4 + 6$
Fifth term is	$5 + 6$
nth term is	$n + 6$

1 The position-to-term rule for a sequence is $n + 4$.

a Find the 20th term.

b Find the 100th term.

2 The position-to-term rule for a sequence is $n - 7$.

a Find the 10th term.

b Find the 50th term.

3 The position-to-term rule for a sequence is $4n$.

a Find the 40th term.

b One term has value 76. Which term is it?

4 Find the nth term of each of these sequences.

a 2, 3, 4, 5, 6, …

b 7, 8, 9, 10, 11, …

c 5, 6, 7, 8, 9, …

d $^{-}3, ^{-}2, ^{-}1, 0, 1, \ldots$

e 4, 8, 12, 16, 20, …

f 6, 12, 18, 24, 30, …

g $^{-}2, ^{-}4, ^{-}6, ^{-}8, ^{-}10, \ldots$

h $^{-}7, ^{-}14, ^{-}21, ^{-}28, ^{-}35, \ldots$

5 The nth term of a sequence is $n - 5$.
How many negative terms are there in the sequence?

6 The position-to-term rule for a sequence is $7 - 3n$.
Write down the first five terms of this sequence.

7 The position-to-term rule for a sequence is $5n - 2$.

a Find the 40th term.

b One term has value 83. Which term is it?

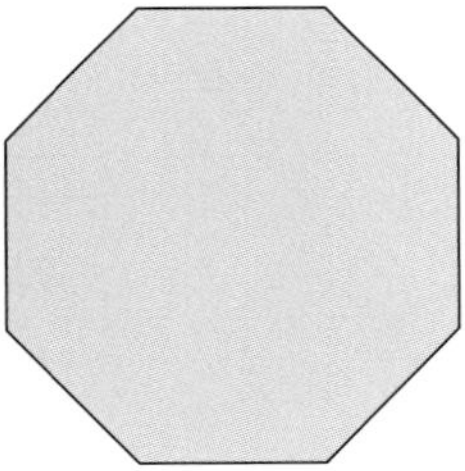4 Draw a grid with the x-axis from $^-6$ to 6 and the y-axis from $^-6$ to 6.
Draw a pentagon ABCDE with vertices:
A = (2, 0) B = (5, 3) C = (0, 6) D = ($^-3$, 5) E = ($^-6$, 1)

a Reflect this pentagon in the x-axis.

b Is your image congruent to pentagon ABCDE? Give reasons for your answer.

5 Reflecting the pattern in the lines made this kaleidoscope pattern.
Make a kaleidoscope pattern of your own.

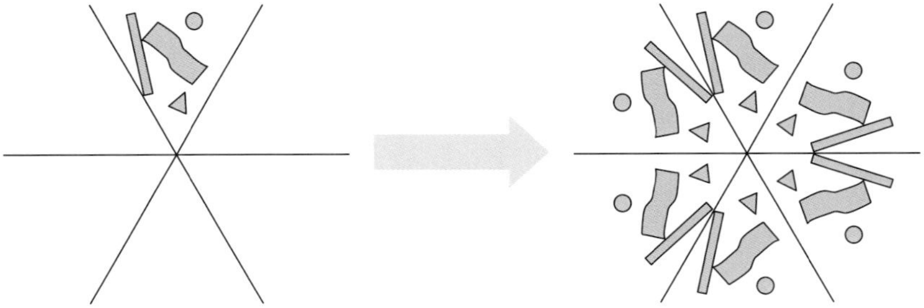

1A Adding and subtracting negative numbers

Example

Work out: **a** $6 + {}^-2$ **b** ${}^-7 - {}^-3$

a $6 + {}^-2 = 6 - 2 = 4$ **b** ${}^-7 - {}^-3 = {}^-7 + 3 = {}^-4$

1 Copy and complete these sequences.

a 5, 3, 1, $^-1$, □, □, □ **b** 30, 23, 16, 9, □, □, □

c $^-36$, $^-31$, $^-26$, $^-21$, □, □, □

2 Work out:

a $6 + {}^-4$ **b** $8 + {}^-7$ **c** $5 + {}^-5$ **d** $8 + {}^-10$

e $9 + {}^-3$ **f** $14 + {}^-8$ **g** $6 + {}^-8$ **h** $2 + {}^-9$

i ${}^-6 + {}^-2$ **j** ${}^-1 + {}^-7$ **k** ${}^-3 + {}^-6$ **l** ${}^-12 + {}^-15$

m ${}^-8 + {}^-5$ **n** ${}^-6 + {}^-11$ **o** ${}^-4 + {}^-9$ **p** ${}^-6 + {}^-6$

3 Work out:

a $6 - {}^-4$ **b** $9 - {}^-2$ **c** $5 - {}^-8$ **d** $1 - {}^-1$

e ${}^-4 - {}^-6$ **f** ${}^-8 - {}^-2$ **g** ${}^-5 - {}^-5$ **h** ${}^-2 - {}^-5$

i ${}^-14 - {}^-8$ **j** ${}^-13 - {}^-11$ **k** ${}^-9 - {}^-32$ **l** ${}^-46 - {}^-18$

4 Work out:

a ${}^-4 + {}^-3 + 8$ **b** ${}^-7 - {}^-5 + {}^-3$ **c** $8 + {}^-5 - {}^-7$

d ${}^-1 + {}^-6 + {}^-9$ **e** $9 - {}^-7 + {}^-4$ **f** $29 - {}^-11 + 9$

g ${}^-6 + {}^-6 - {}^-6$ **h** $11 - {}^-22 + {}^-33$ **i** ${}^-2 - {}^-6 + {}^-9$

5 Copy and complete:

a $7 - \square = {}^-2$ **b** $\square + 7 = {}^-23$ **c** $15 + \square = 6$

d $\square + {}^-11 = {}^-16$ **e** $12 + \square = {}^-14$ **f** $\square + {}^-26 = {}^-2$

6 Work out: $15 + {}^-8 - 2 + {}^-6$

7 Write down five different numbers that add together to give the number $^-3$.

8 Numbers in squares = the sum of numbers in circles. Find the missing numbers.

a

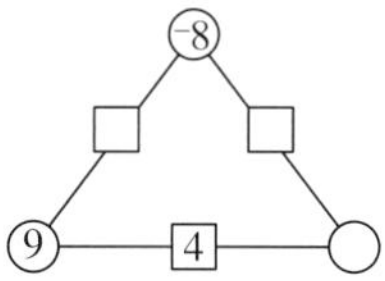

b

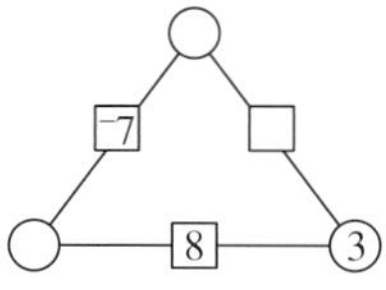

c

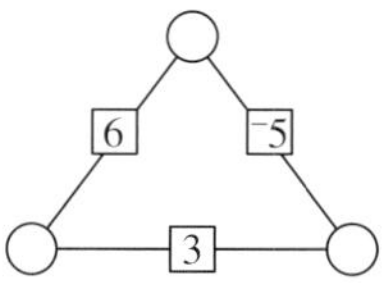

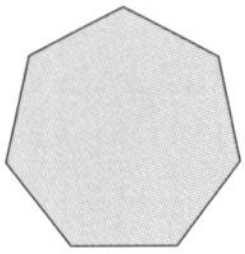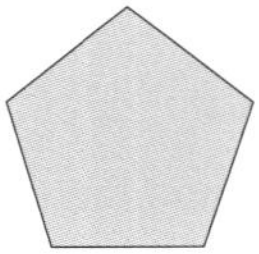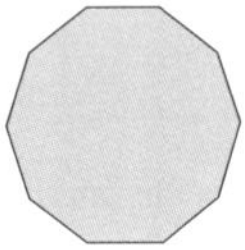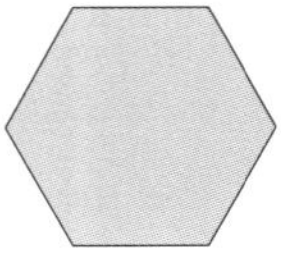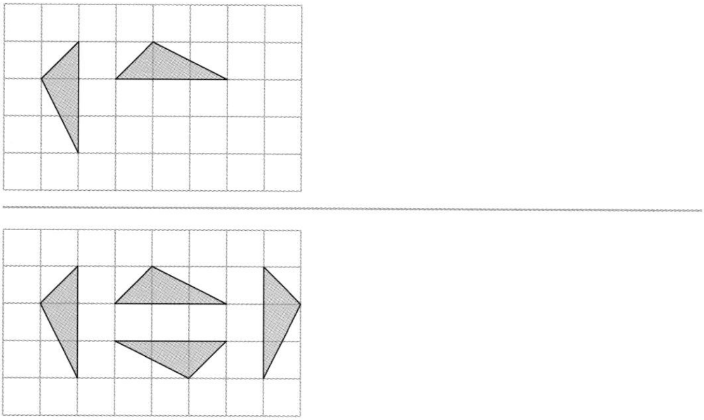

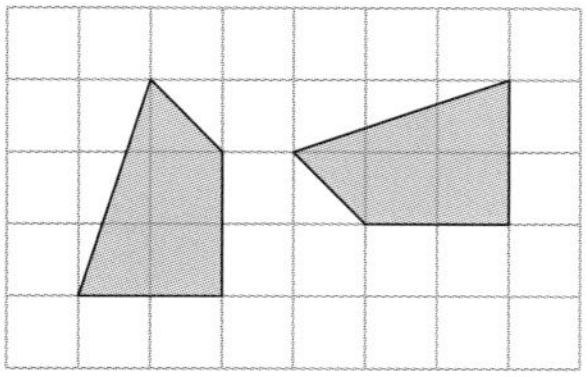

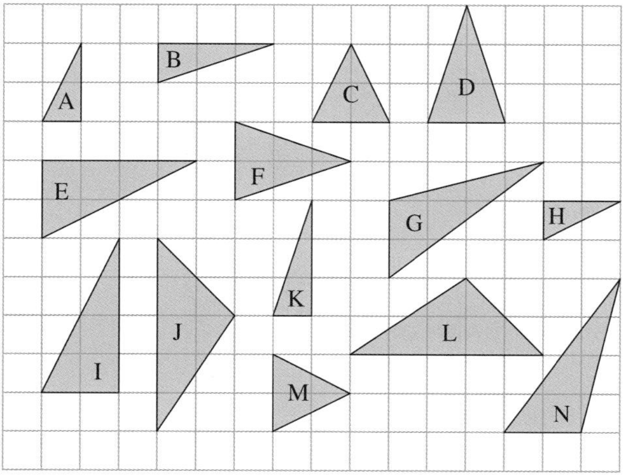

7G Using equations to solve problems

Example

The length of a rectangle is three times its width.
The perimeter of the rectangle is 72 cm.
Find the width of the rectangle.

$$\begin{aligned} \text{Perimeter} &= 72 \\ 3x + x + 3x + x &= 72 \\ 8x &= 72 \\ x &= 9 \end{aligned}$$

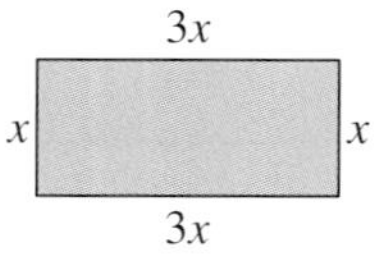

Width = 9 cm

1 For each of these statements, form an equation in x then solve it to find x.

a If we multiply x by 4 the answer is 52.

b If we multiply x by 3 and then add 6 the answer is 27.

c If we multiply x by 2 and then take away 8 the answer is 10.

d If we multiply x by 7 and then add $\frac{1}{2}$ the answer is 18.

2 The length of a rectangle is twice its width.
The perimeter is 54 cm.

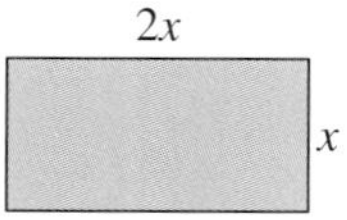

a Write down an equation in x.

b Solve your equation to find the value of x.

3 This rectangle has a perimeter of 60 cm.

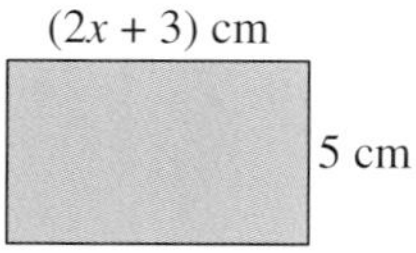

a Write down an equation in x.

b Solve your equation to find the value of x.

7H Inequalities

Example

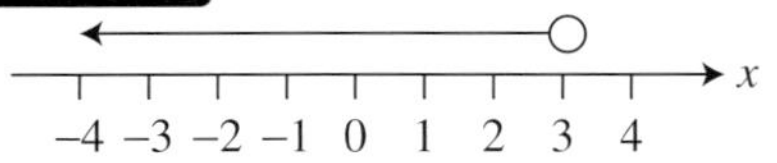

a Write down the inequality shown by this number line.
b Write down the largest integer x could be.

a All the values on the arrow are smaller than 3 so $x < 3$.
b The largest integer x could be is 2.

1 Copy and complete the following, using < or > in place of the boxes.

a $5 \square 8$ **b** $7 \square 2$ **c** $^{-}1 \square 3$

d $15 \square 6$ **e** $^{-}7 \square {}^{-}9$ **f** $^{-}2 \square 6$

2 Represent these inequalities on a number line.

a $x > 2$ **b** $x < 4$

3 Write down the inequalities shown on these number lines.

a

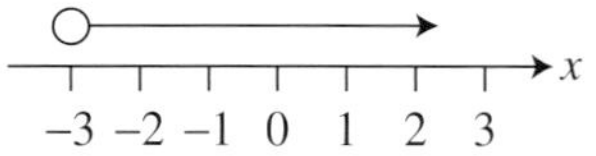

b

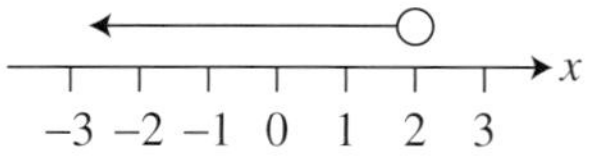

c

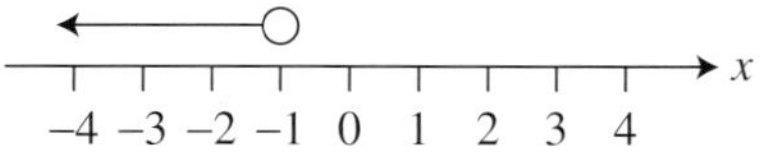

4 **a** What is the smallest integer that x could be in question **3a**?

b What is the largest integer that x could be in question **3b**?

c What is the largest integer that x could be in question **3c**?

5 What is the smallest negative integer that satisfies the inequality $x > {}^{-}4$?

1B Multiplying and dividing negative numbers

Example

Work out: **a** $4 \times {}^-3$ **b** ${}^-40 \div 5$

a $4 \times {}^-3 = {}^-12$ **b** ${}^-40 \div 5 = {}^-8$

1 Work out:

a $6 \times {}^-4$ **b** $8 \times {}^-7$ **c** $5 \times {}^-5$ **d** $8 \times {}^-10$

e $9 \times {}^-3$ **f** $14 \times {}^-8$ **g** $6 \times {}^-8$ **h** $2 \times {}^-9$

i ${}^-4 \times 8$ **j** ${}^-11 \times 5$ **k** ${}^-9 \times 3$ **l** ${}^-16 \times 5$

2 Work out:

a $4 \times {}^-3 \times 2$ **b** ${}^-2 \times 5 \times 3$ **c** $4 \times {}^-1 \times 3$

d ${}^-1 \times 6 \times 9$ **e** $2 \times {}^-7 \times 4$ **f** $5 \times {}^-11 \times 2$

3 Work out:

$92 \times {}^-37 \times 43 \times 0 \times 17$

4 Find the missing numbers.

a ${}^-5 \times \square = {}^-20$ **b** $\square \times 6 = {}^-72$

5 Work out:

a $8 \div {}^-4$ **b** $15 \div {}^-3$ **c** $18 \div {}^-2$ **d** $20 \div {}^-10$

e $9 \div {}^-3$ **f** $40 \div {}^-8$ **g** $64 \div {}^-8$ **h** $27 \div {}^-9$

i ${}^-48 \div 8$ **j** ${}^-35 \div 5$ **k** ${}^-42 \div 3$ **l** ${}^-75 \div 5$

6 Work out:

a $\frac{{}^-16}{4}$ **b** $\frac{{}^-24}{3}$ **c** $\frac{8}{{}^-2}$ **d** $\frac{75}{{}^-15}$

7 Work out:

a $\frac{3 \times {}^-4}{4}$ **b** $\frac{8 \times {}^-3}{{}^-5 + 7}$ **c** $\frac{16}{{}^-2} + \frac{{}^-20}{2}$ **d** ${}^-8 - \frac{{}^-18}{3}$

e $\frac{{}^-2 + {}^-8}{5}$ **f** $\frac{45}{{}^-3} \div \frac{27}{9}$ **g** $\frac{2 - {}^-4}{16 \div 8}$ **h** ${}^-5 + \frac{{}^-10}{5} + {}^-8$

2F Expanding brackets

Example

Expand the brackets: **a** $5(2x + 4)$ **b** $^{-}3(2x - 7)$

a $5(2x + 4) = 10x + 20$

b $^{-}3(2x - 7) = {}^{-}6x + 21$

1 Expand the brackets.

a $3(x + 2)$ **b** $4(y - 5)$ **c** $5(8 + a)$

d $6(3 - p)$ **e** $2(x + y)$ **f** $3(a - b)$

g $8(m - n)$ **h** $7(p + q)$ **i** $6(2x + 1)$

j $5(3y - 2)$ **k** $4(6 - 5y)$ **l** $2(3v - 4)$

m $3(2x + 3y)$ **n** $4(6x - 5y)$ **o** $9(4a + 5b)$

p $8(3p - 4q)$ **q** $^{-}2(x + 2)$ **r** $^{-}4(y - 1)$

s $^{-}3(4y + 7)$ **t** $^{-}2(6 - 5y)$

2 Expand the brackets.

a $4(2a + 3b - 5)$ **b** $3(5x - 2y + z)$ **c** $6(1 + 2x + 3y)$

d $2(5p - 3 + 2q)$ **e** $7(3f + 2g - 5h)$ **f** $10(x - 2y + 3z)$

g $^{-}3(2x + y - 4)$ **h** $^{-}2(a - 3b + 7)$ **i** $^{-}7(3p - q + 4r)$

3 Expand the brackets.

a $\frac{1}{2}(4x + 6)$ **b** $\frac{1}{2}(8y - 10)$ **c** $\frac{1}{3}(6x - 9)$

d $\frac{1}{5}(20x - 15)$ **e** $\frac{1}{4}(28x + 4)$ **f** $\frac{1}{8}(16 - 40x)$

4 Copy and complete:

a $3(2x + \square) = 6x + 15$ **b** $4(3y - \square) = 12y - 8$

c $8(6x - \square) = 48x - 56$ **d** $5(\square - 2y) = 25 - 10y$

e $6(\square x + 3) = 12x + 18$ **f** $\square(7x + 2) = 28x + 8$

g $\square(5y - 4) = {}^{-}15y + 12$ **h** $^{-}8(\square x + 5) = {}^{-}16x - 40$

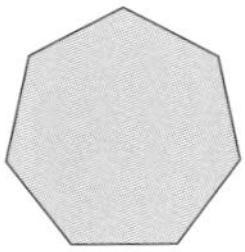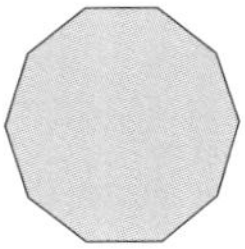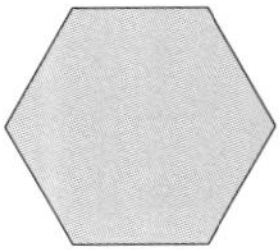## 8E Distance between coordinates

Example

Find the distance between the points A = ($^-2$, $^-4$) and B = (9, $^-4$).

The y-coordinates are the same for both A and B, which means A and B lie on the same horizontal line, $y = {}^-4$.

Point B is 9 units to the right of the y-axis and point A is 2 units to the left of the y-axis.

Distance between A and B = 9 + 2 = 11

Try to do all of these questions without drawing on squared paper.

1 Which of these points lie on the same **vertical** line?

a ($^-3$, 1) **b** (1, $^-3$) **c** (2, $^-2$) **d** (1, 5)

e ($^-2$, $^-2$) **f** (1, 0) **g** (3, 0) **h** ($^-1$, 1)

2 Which of these points lie on the same **horizontal** line?

a ($^-4$, 4) **b** ($^-2$, 2) **c** (2, 0) **d** ($^-4$, $^-2$) **e** (5, $^-2$)

f (2, 3) **g** (0, $^-2$) **h** ($^-4$, 1) **i** (2, $^-2$) **j** (0, 6)

3 Find the distance between these pairs of points.

a (6, 3) and (6, 10) **b** (1, 8) and (1, 5) **c** (0, $^-2$) and (0, $^-7$)

d ($^-3$, 2) and ($^-3$, $^-4$) **e** (2, $^-4$) and ($^-11$, $^-4$) **f** ($^-4$, $^-4$) and ($^-4$, $^-14$)

4 The coordinates of three of the vertices of a square are (5, 6), ($^-3$, 6) and ($^-3$, $^-2$).
Write down the coordinates of the fourth vertex.

5 Triangle ABC is a right-angled isosceles triangle with AC = AB.
The coordinates of vertices A and B are A = ($^-3$, $^-2$) and B = ($^-3$, 6).
Write down the two possible positions for the vertex C.

6 ABC is an isosceles triangle with AC = BC.
The coordinates of vertices A and B are A = (5, 6) and B = ($^-1$, 6).
Write down three possible positions for the vertex C.

7 ABCD is a parallelogram.
The coordinates of vertices A, B and C are A = (1, 5), B = ($^-2$, 4) and C = ($^-4$, 0).
Write down the coordinates of vertex D.

8 The coordinates of three of the vertices of a rectangle are ($^-1$, 0), ($^-2$, 2) and (2, 4).
Write down the coordinates of the fourth vertex.

12C The *n*th term

Example

Find the nth term for the sequence 7, 8, 9, 10, 11, ...

First term is	$1+6$
Second term is	$2+6$
Third term is	$3+6$
Fourth term is	$4+6$
Fifth term is	$5+6$
nth term is	$n+6$

1 The position-to-term rule for a sequence is $n+4$.

a Find the 20th term.

b Find the 100th term.

2 The position-to-term rule for a sequence is $n-7$.

a Find the 10th term.

b Find the 50th term.

3 The position-to-term rule for a sequence is $4n$.

a Find the 40th term.

b One term has value 76. Which term is it?

4 Find the nth term of each of these sequences.

a 2, 3, 4, 5, 6, …

b 7, 8, 9, 10, 11, …

c 5, 6, 7, 8, 9, …

d $^-3, ^-2, ^-1, 0, 1$, …

e 4, 8, 12, 16, 20, …

f 6, 12, 18, 24, 30, …

g $^-2, ^-4, ^-6, ^-8, ^-10$, ...

h $^-7, ^-14, ^-21, ^-28, ^-35$, …

5 The nth term of a sequence is $n-5$.
How many negative terms are there in the sequence?

6 The position-to-term rule for a sequence is $7-3n$.
Write down the first five terms of this sequence.

7 The position-to-term rule for a sequence is $5n-2$.

a Find the 40th term.

b One term has value 83. Which term is it?

12F Horizontal and vertical lines

Example

Draw the graph of $y = 2$.

Every point on the line $y = 2$ will have a y-coordinate of 2.
Some of these points are: (3, 2), (1, 2), (⁻3, 2), (2, 2).
Plot the points on a pair of axes and join with a straight line.

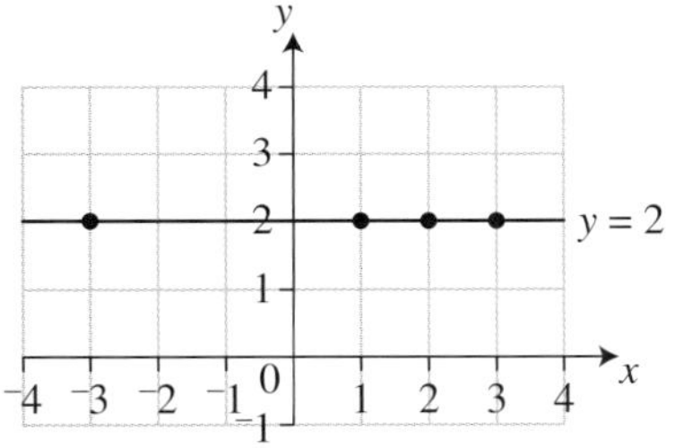

1 Plot the points (3, 4), (1, 4), (⁻3, 4), (2, 4) and (⁻1, 4) on a pair of axes.
What is the equation of the straight line that passes through these five points?

2 Plot the points (⁻3, 5), (⁻3, ⁻3), (⁻3, 1), (⁻3, ⁻5) and (⁻3, 4) on a pair of axes.
What is the equation of the straight line that passes through these five points?

3 Write down the equations of the lines A, B, C, D, E and F.

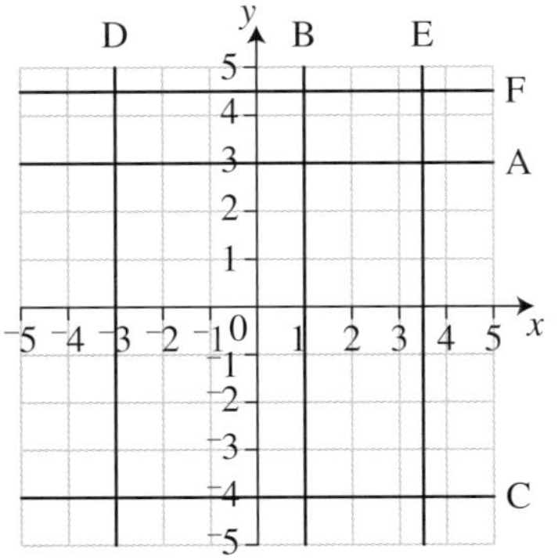

4 For each set of coordinates, write down an equation for the line that passes through all of them.

a (⁻2, 4), (⁻2, ⁻3), (⁻2, 8), (⁻2, ⁻5), (⁻2, ⁻7)

b (3, 3), (⁻3, ⁻3), (5, 5), (0, 0), (⁻2, ⁻2)

c (2, 6), (3, 9), (1, 3), (0, 0), (5, 15)

d (1, 7), (2, 12), (3, 17), (4, 22), (10, 52)

5 Describe the translation that maps:

a (5, 1) onto (3, 7)

b (3, $^-4$) onto ($^-5$, 8)

6 Draw a pair of axes from 0 to 10.

a Draw a triangle with vertices (1, 1), (3, 1) and (3, 4).
Label this triangle A.

b Translate triangle A 6 right and 2 up. Label this image B.

c Translate triangle B 3 left and 3 up. Label this image C.

d Describe the translation that would take triangle A directly onto triangle C.

7 These are the coordinates of three of the vertices of a parallelogram ABCD:

A = (5, 4) B = ($^-3$, 5) C = ($^-6$, 1)

The parallelogram is translated 4 right and 3 down, to the image A′B′C′D′.
What are the coordinates of D′, the image of the fourth vertex?

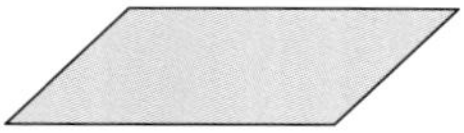

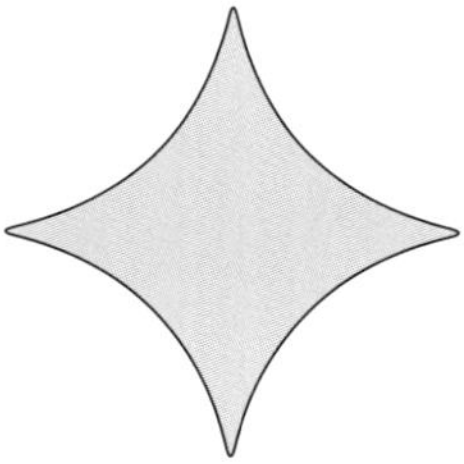

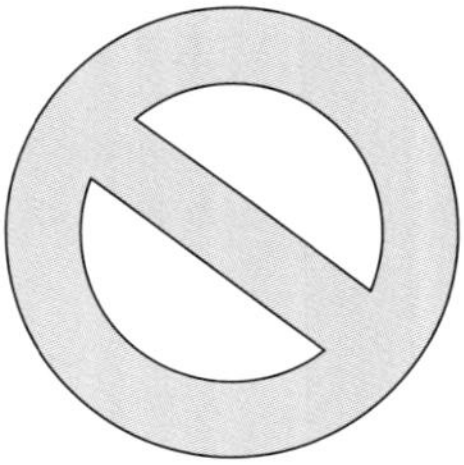

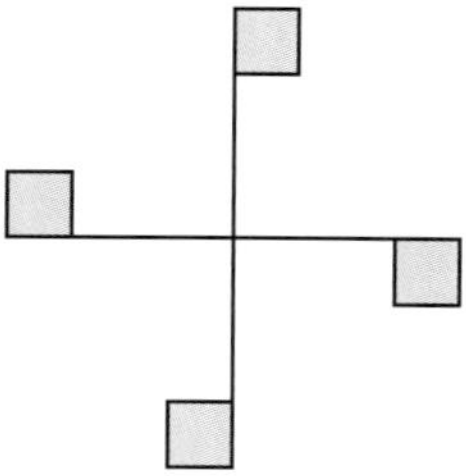

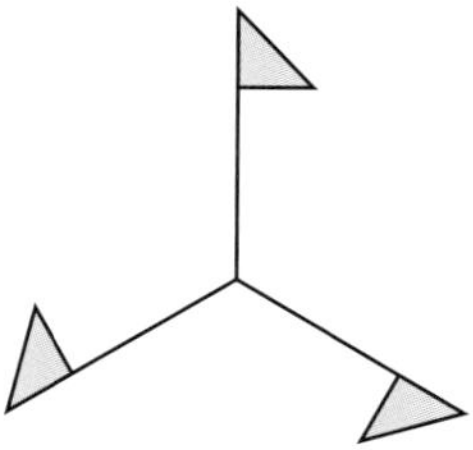

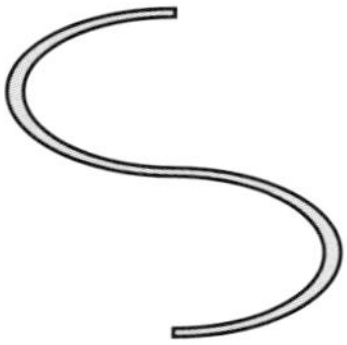

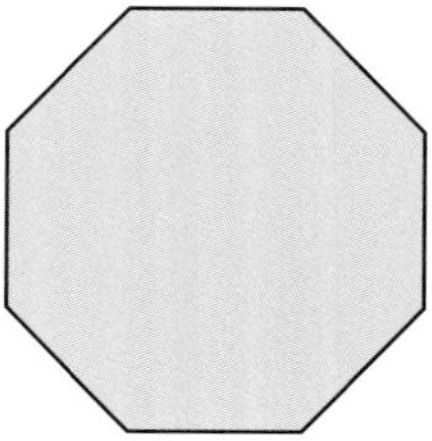

1F Divisibility tests

Example

A number is divisible by 3 if the sum of its digits is divisible by 3.

a Is 348 divisible by 3? **b** Is 1927 divisible by 3?

a $3+4+8=15$
15 is divisible by 3
so 348 is divisible by 3

b $1+9+2+7=19$
19 is not divisible by 3 so
1927 is not divisible by 3

Use divisibility tests to answer these questions.

1 Which of these numbers are divisible by 3?

a 51 **b** 82 **c** 104 **d** 117
e 162 **f** 451 **g** 845 **h** 6432

2 Which of these numbers are divisible by 5?

a 87 **b** 45 **c** 236 **d** 439
e 545 **f** 1068 **g** 6534 **h** 9875

3 Which of these numbers are divisible by 2?

a 77 **b** 98 **c** 114 **d** 237
e 86 **f** 779 **g** 5243 **h** 6766

4 A number is divisible by 4 if the number formed from the last two digits is divisible by 4. Which of these numbers are divisible by 4?

a 308 **b** 244 **c** 555 **d** 236
e 783 **f** 6520 **g** 7654 **h** 9888

5 A number is divisible by 9 if the sum of its digits is divisible by 9. Which of these numbers are divisible by 9?

a 126 **b** 415 **c** 368 **d** 675
e 2377 **f** 6666 **g** 9162 **h** 7557

6 A number is divisible by 6 if it is an even number **and** the sum of its digits is divisible by 3. Which of these numbers are divisible by 6?

a 84 **b** 426 **c** 252 **d** 441
e 783 **f** 722 **g** 6432 **h** 8116

7 How can you test whether a 3-digit number is divisible by 11?

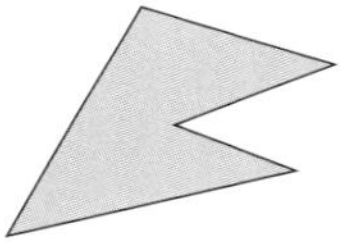

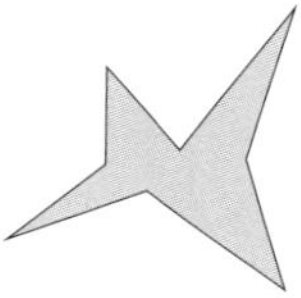

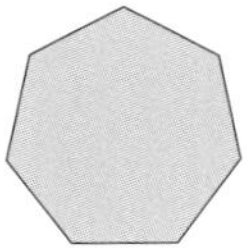

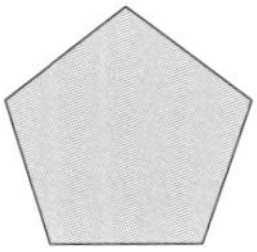

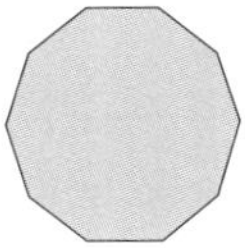

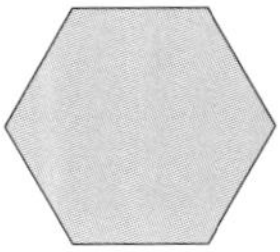

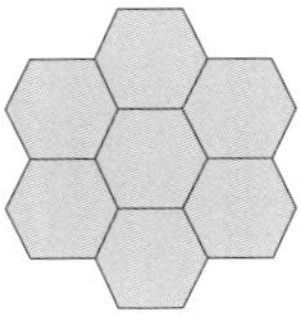

5 **a** Find the volume of this cuboid in m^3.

b Write down the volume of the cuboid in cm^3.

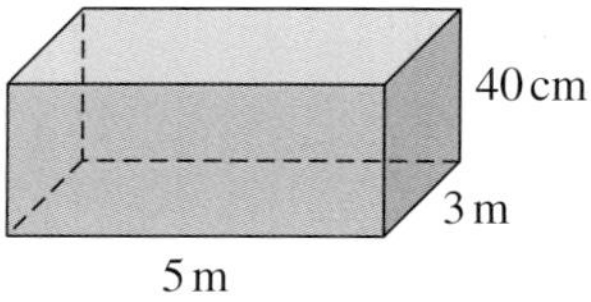

6 Find the volume of this shape. All lengths are in cm.

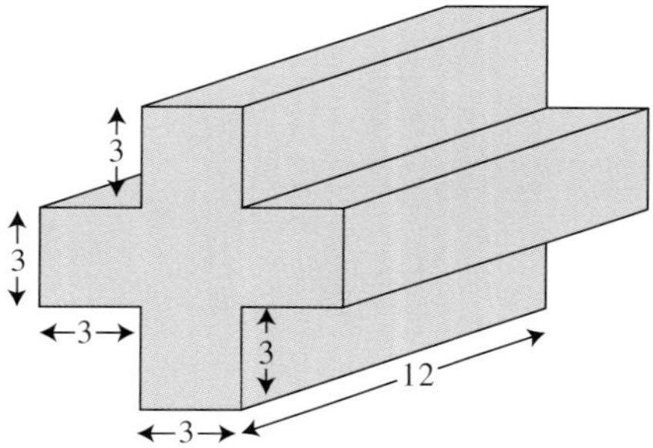

7 Find the missing side lengths in each of these cuboids.

a

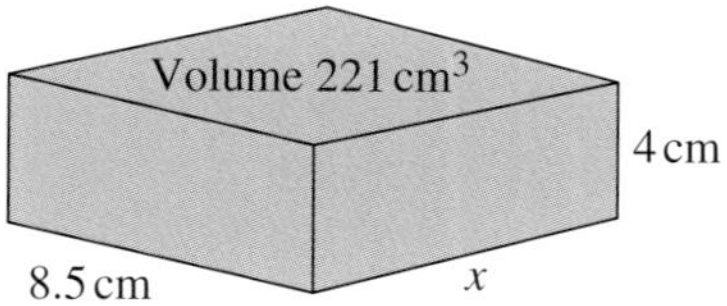

b

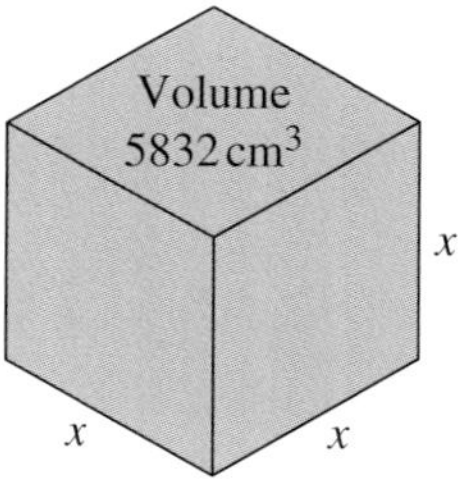

8 Find the volume of this triangular prism.

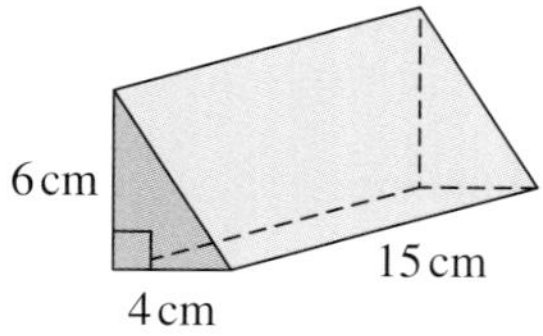

The triangular prism is half of a cuboid.

9 The volume of this shape is $1232\,cm^3$.
Find the value of x.

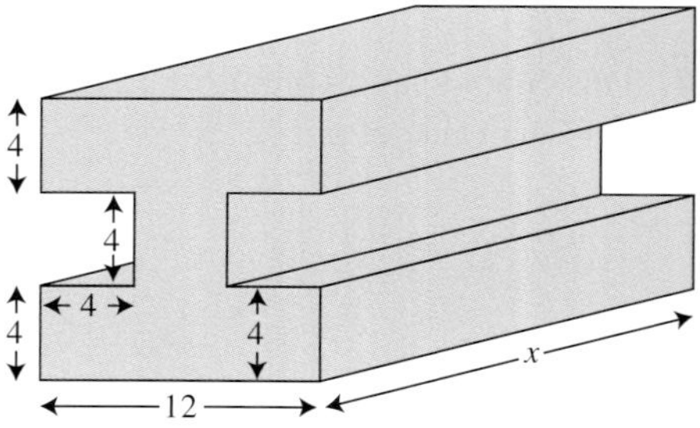

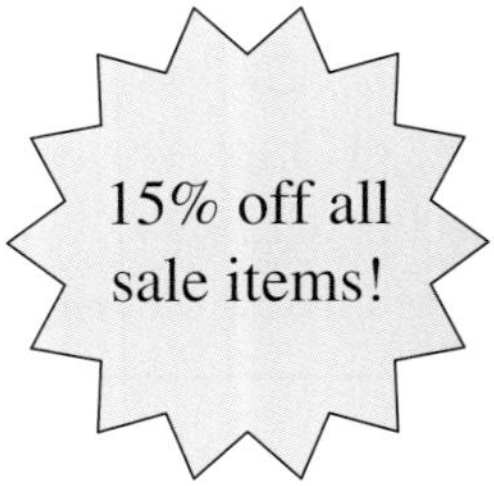

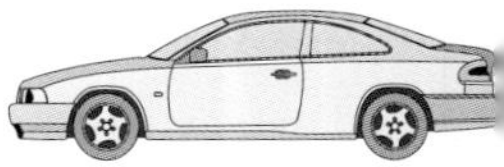

11A Simplifying ratios

Example

Write each ratio in its simplest form.

a $64:38$ **b** $7:0.3$ **c** $\frac{2}{5}:\frac{7}{10}$

a $64:38$ $\xrightarrow{\div 2}$ $32:19$

b $7:0.3$ $\xrightarrow{\times 10}$ $70:3$

c $\frac{2}{5}:\frac{7}{10}$ $\xrightarrow{\times 10}$ $4:7$

1 Write each ratio in its simplest form.

a $3:6$ **b** $7:14$ **c** $8:4$ **d** $27:18$

e $6:8$ **f** $35:20$ **g** $28:20$ **h** $50:20$

i $15:10$ **j** $64:24$ **k** $49:63$ **l** $50:250$

m $21:15$ **n** $32:36$ **o** $231:111$ **p** $392:413$

2 Match equivalent pairs of ratios. Find the odd one out.

7:14	12:9	3:1	20:24	
5:6	52:13	6:7	21:18	1:2
4:3	42:14	7:6	4:1	

3 Write each ratio in its simplest form.

a $12:18:24$ **b** $35:14:7$ **c** $96:36:60$ **d** $400:50:250$

4 Write each ratio in its simplest form.

a $0.3:2$ **b** $0.8:5$ **c** $7:1.3$ **d** $4.6:8.4$

e $0.6:0.3:0.7$ **f** $0.5:4:1.5$ **g** $1.2:0.8:4$ **h** $5.5:8:2.5$

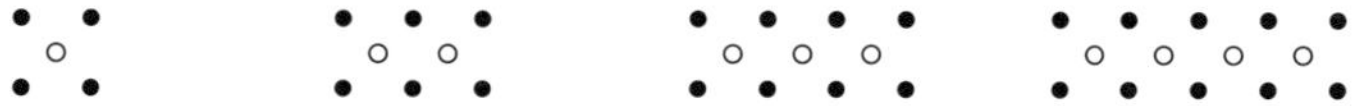

   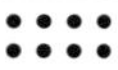   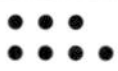 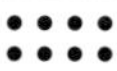    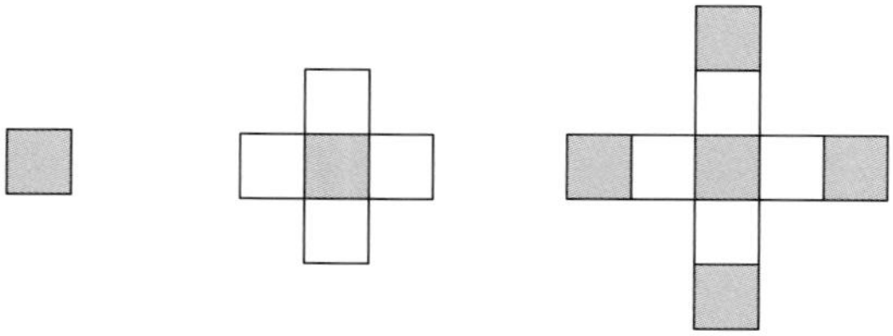

12C The *n*th term

Example

Find the nth term for the sequence 7, 8, 9, 10, 11, ...

First term is	$1+6$
Second term is	$2+6$
Third term is	$3+6$
Fourth term is	$4+6$
Fifth term is	$5+6$
nth term is	$n+6$

1 The position-to-term rule for a sequence is $n+4$.

a Find the 20th term.

b Find the 100th term.

2 The position-to-term rule for a sequence is $n-7$.

a Find the 10th term.

b Find the 50th term.

3 The position-to-term rule for a sequence is $4n$.

a Find the 40th term.

b One term has value 76. Which term is it?

4 Find the nth term of each of these sequences.

a 2, 3, 4, 5, 6, …

b 7, 8, 9, 10, 11, …

c 5, 6, 7, 8, 9, …

d $^{-}3, ^{-}2, ^{-}1, 0, 1$, …

e 4, 8, 12, 16, 20, …

f 6, 12, 18, 24, 30, …

g $^{-}2, ^{-}4, ^{-}6, ^{-}8, ^{-}10$, ...

h $^{-}7, ^{-}14, ^{-}21, ^{-}28, ^{-}35$, …

5 The nth term of a sequence is $n-5$.
How many negative terms are there in the sequence?

6 The position-to-term rule for a sequence is $7-3n$.
Write down the first five terms of this sequence.

7 The position-to-term rule for a sequence is $5n-2$.

a Find the 40th term.

b One term has value 83. Which term is it?

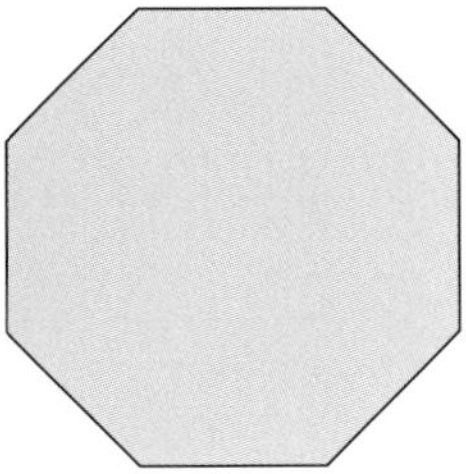# 1A Adding and subtracting negative numbers

Example

Work out: **a** $6 + {}^{-}2$ **b** ${}^{-}7 - {}^{-}3$

a $6 + {}^{-}2 = 6 - 2 = 4$ **b** ${}^{-}7 - {}^{-}3 = {}^{-}7 + 3 = {}^{-}4$

1 Copy and complete these sequences.

a $5,\ 3,\ 1,\ {}^{-}1,\ \square,\ \square,\ \square$ **b** $30,\ 23,\ 16,\ 9,\ \square,\ \square,\ \square$

c ${}^{-}36,\ {}^{-}31,\ {}^{-}26,\ {}^{-}21,\ \square,\ \square,\ \square$

2 Work out:

a $6 + {}^{-}4$ **b** $8 + {}^{-}7$ **c** $5 + {}^{-}5$ **d** $8 + {}^{-}10$

e $9 + {}^{-}3$ **f** $14 + {}^{-}8$ **g** $6 + {}^{-}8$ **h** $2 + {}^{-}9$

i ${}^{-}6 + {}^{-}2$ **j** ${}^{-}1 + {}^{-}7$ **k** ${}^{-}3 + {}^{-}6$ **l** ${}^{-}12 + {}^{-}15$

m ${}^{-}8 + {}^{-}5$ **n** ${}^{-}6 + {}^{-}11$ **o** ${}^{-}4 + {}^{-}9$ **p** ${}^{-}6 + {}^{-}6$

3 Work out:

a $6 - {}^{-}4$ **b** $9 - {}^{-}2$ **c** $5 - {}^{-}8$ **d** $1 - {}^{-}1$

e ${}^{-}4 - {}^{-}6$ **f** ${}^{-}8 - {}^{-}2$ **g** ${}^{-}5 - {}^{-}5$ **h** ${}^{-}2 - {}^{-}5$

i ${}^{-}14 - {}^{-}8$ **j** ${}^{-}13 - {}^{-}11$ **k** ${}^{-}9 - {}^{-}32$ **l** ${}^{-}46 - {}^{-}18$

4 Work out:

a ${}^{-}4 + {}^{-}3 + 8$ **b** ${}^{-}7 - {}^{-}5 + {}^{-}3$ **c** $8 + {}^{-}5 - {}^{-}7$

d ${}^{-}1 + {}^{-}6 + {}^{-}9$ **e** $9 - {}^{-}7 + {}^{-}4$ **f** $29 - {}^{-}11 + 9$

g ${}^{-}6 + {}^{-}6 - {}^{-}6$ **h** $11 - {}^{-}22 + {}^{-}33$ **i** ${}^{-}2 - {}^{-}6 + {}^{-}9$

5 Copy and complete:

a $7 - \square = {}^{-}2$ **b** $\square + 7 = {}^{-}23$ **c** $15 + \square = 6$

d $\square + {}^{-}11 = {}^{-}16$ **e** $12 + \square = {}^{-}14$ **f** $\square + {}^{-}26 = {}^{-}2$

6 Work out: $15 + {}^{-}8 - 2 + {}^{-}6$

7 Write down five different numbers that add together to give the number ${}^{-}3$.

8 Numbers in squares = the sum of numbers in circles. Find the missing numbers.

a

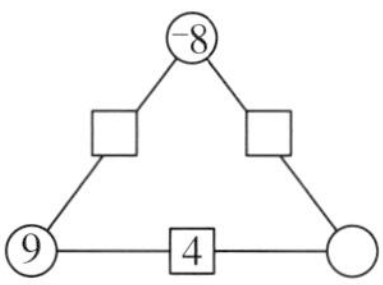

b

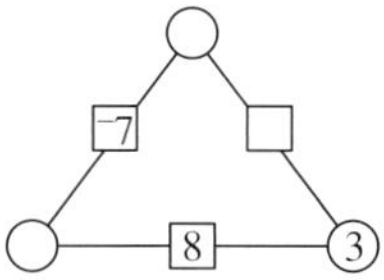

c

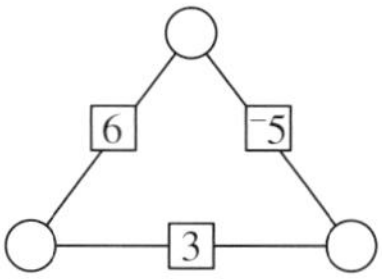

1D Order of operations

Example

Work out $18 - (5 - 2) \times 4$

$18 - (5 - 2) \times 4 = 18 - 3 \times 4$ **B**rackets first, then

$= 18 - 12$ **M**ultiplication

$= 6$

1 Work out:

a $9 - 2 \times 3$ **b** $6 + 5 \times 4$ **c** $24 \div 6 - 2$

d $4 + 18 \div 2$ **e** $11 + 2 \times 9$ **f** $30 - 16 \div 4$

g $10 - 36 \times 2$ **h** $15 - 4 \times 7$ **i** $2 - 52 \div 4$

j $1 + 2 \times 3 + 4$ **k** $5 + 3 \times 6 - 9$ **l** $7 + 3 \times 2 - 4$

m $7 - 36 \div 9 + 2$ **n** $8 + 20 \div 5 - 3$ **o** $4 \times 5 + 6 \times 7$

p $3 \times 4 + 15 \div 3$ **q** $10 \div 2 + 3 \times 4$ **r** $18 \div 9 - 20 \div 4$

2 Work out:

a $2 \times (3 + 4)$ **b** $5 + (8 \div 2)$ **c** $3 \times (18 \div 2)$

d $40 \div (12 - 8)$ **e** $2 \times (8 - 5) \times 4$ **f** $5 - (82 - 50)$

g $(12 + 2) \times (13 + 7)$ **h** $(8 + 4) \div (7 - 5)$ **i** $8 \times (9 + 3) \times 5$

3 Work out:

a $5 + 2 \times 6$ **b** $2 - 12 \div 4$ **c** $6 + 5^2 \times 2$

d $4^3 + 6 \times {}^-3$ **e** $10^2 \times (6 - 10)$ **f** ${}^-2 \times {}^-3 + 4$

g $48 \div {}^-2 + 7 \times 2$ **h** $10 \div {}^-5 - {}^-2$ **i** ${}^-5 + 2^3 \times 3^2 - 17$

4 Copy these and insert brackets to make the statements correct.

a $5 \times 6 + 7 = 65$ **b** $20 - 12 \div 4 = 2$

c $12 \times 9 - 8 \times 2 = 24$ **d** $7 \times 2 - 10 \div 2 = 2$

e $14 - 10 \div 2 = 2$ **f** $9 + 6 \times 8 - 5 = 45$

1G–1I Square and cube roots

Example

Work out $\sqrt{81} + \sqrt{49}$

$\sqrt{81} + \sqrt{49} = 9 + 7 = 16$

1 Write down the value of:

a $\sqrt{25}$ **b** $\sqrt{81}$ **c** $\sqrt{16}$ **d** $\sqrt{289}$

2 Work out the value of:

a 2^2 **b** 3^2 **c** 7^2 **d** 15^2

e $({}^{-}2)^2$ **f** $({}^{-}3)^2$ **g** $({}^{-}7)^2$ **h** $({}^{-}15)^2$

3 Work out:

a $\sqrt{36}$ **b** $\sqrt{64}$ **c** $\sqrt{100}$ **d** $\sqrt{144}$

e $\sqrt{81} + \sqrt{4}$ **f** $\sqrt{49} - \sqrt{16}$ **g** $\sqrt{4} \times \sqrt{9}$ **h** $\sqrt{100} \surd \sqrt{4}$

i $\sqrt{9 + 16}$ **j** $\sqrt{9} + \sqrt{16}$ **k** $\sqrt{100 - 36}$ **l** $\sqrt{100} - \sqrt{36}$

m $\sqrt{4 \times 25}$ **n** $\sqrt{4} \times \sqrt{25}$ **o** $\sqrt{36 \surd 4}$ **p** $\sqrt{36} \surd \sqrt{4}$

4 Write down the lengths of the sides of each of these squares.

a Area $= 81\,\text{cm}^2$

b Area $= 169\,\text{cm}^2$

5 Write down the value of:

a $\sqrt[3]{27}$ **b** $\sqrt[3]{8}$ **c** $\sqrt[3]{{}^{-}64}$ **d** $\sqrt[3]{{}^{-}1000}$

6 Use a calculator to work out:

a 1.2^3 **b** 2.5^3 **c** $({}^{-}6.1)^3$ **d** $({}^{-}0.3)^3$

e $\sqrt[3]{74.088}$ **f** $\sqrt[3]{0.343}$ **g** $\sqrt[3]{4096}$ **h** $\sqrt[3]{13.824}$

7 Use a calculator to find the value of x for each of these cubes.

a

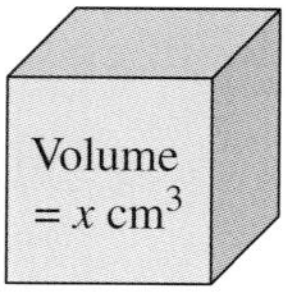

b

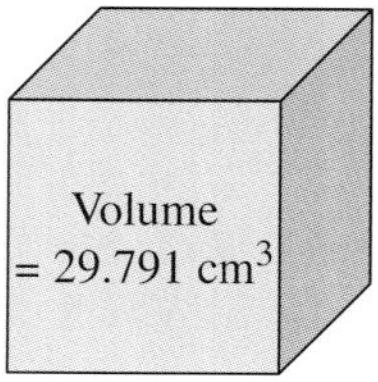

8 Work out the value of:

a $\sqrt{\frac{9}{49}}$ **b** $\sqrt{\frac{16}{25}}$ **c** $\sqrt{0.36}$ **d** $\sqrt{0.09}$

e $\sqrt[3]{\frac{8}{27}}$ **f** $\sqrt[3]{\frac{64}{125}}$ **g** $\sqrt[3]{\frac{1}{64}}$ **h** $\sqrt[3]{0.008}$

2G–2H Expanding and simplifying

Example

Simplify: **a** $3(5x+6)+2(3x+4)$
b $9(3y-4)-2(7y+2)$

a $3(5x+6)+2(3x+4) = 15x+18+6x+8$
$= 21x+26$

b $9(3y-4)-2(7y+2) = 27y-36-14y-4 = 13y-40$

1 Simplify:

a $2(x+3)+3(x+5)$ **b** $5(x+2)+4(x+8)$ **c** $3(y+4)+7(y+7)$

d $6(x-5)+3(x+6)$ **e** $3(x+4)+2(x-5)$ **f** $2(3y+1)+4(2y+5)$

g $3(5x+6)+5(3x+2)$ **h** $2(3x+4)-3(x+2)$ **i** $4(2y-1)+3(2y-5)$

j $5(x+4)-2(x-3)$ **k** $3(5-2x)+4(2x-1)$ **l** $8(4x-5)-3(8-5x)$

m $2+3(x+2)$ **n** $7+3(x+5)$ **o** $14+2(3x-5)+5x$

p $8-5(x+2)$ **q** $6x-(2+x)$ **r** $4x-(2x-5)$

2 **A** $3x+4$ **B** $2x+1$ **C** $x-5$

Use the expressions above in the following, and then simplify:

a $3\mathbf{A}+2\mathbf{B}$ **b** $3\mathbf{B}-2\mathbf{C}$ **c** $5+2\mathbf{A}$ **d** $2\mathbf{A}+\mathbf{B}-3\mathbf{C}$

3 Write an expression for the area of this rectangle.

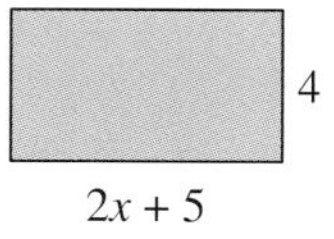

4 Find the area and perimeter of this shape.

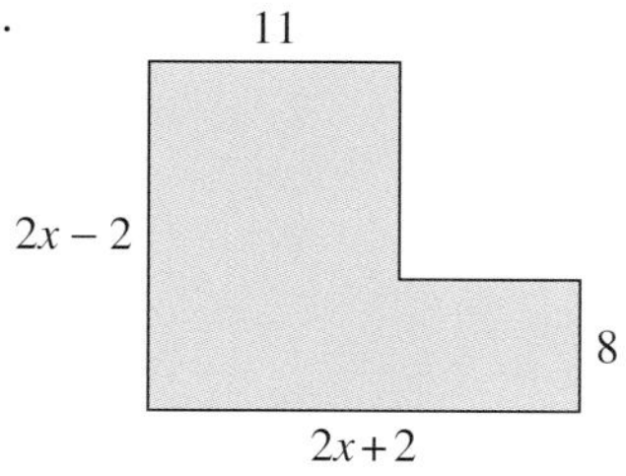

5 Expand and simplify:

a $\frac{1}{2}(10x+8)+\frac{1}{3}(6x+18)$ **b** $\frac{1}{4}(32x-8)+\frac{1}{5}(15x+20)$

6 Copy and complete: $5(x+\square)+\square(x+3)=7x+21$

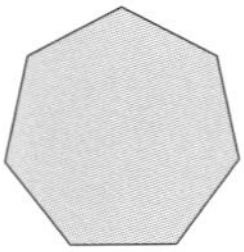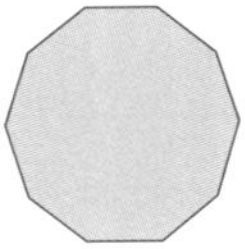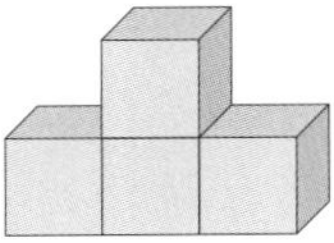

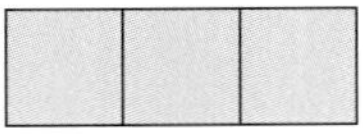

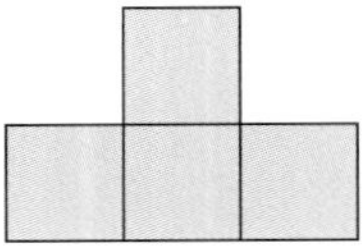

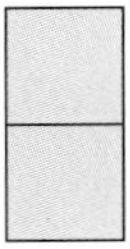

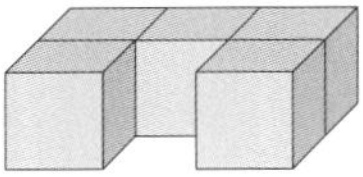

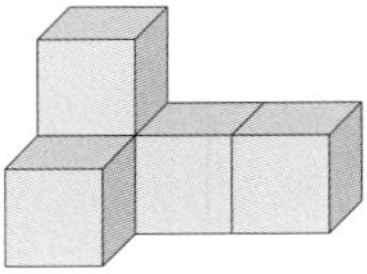

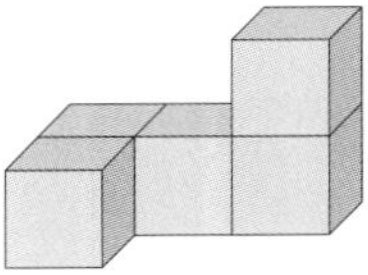

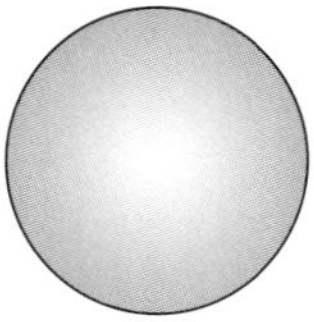

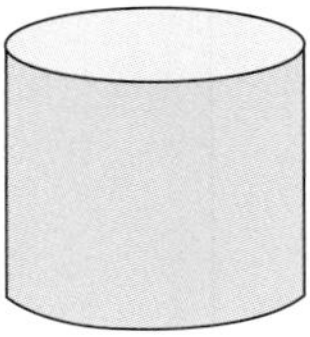

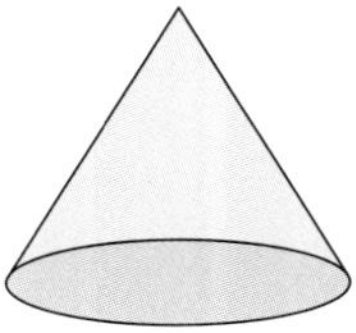

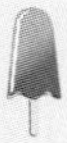  ## 7H Inequalities

Example

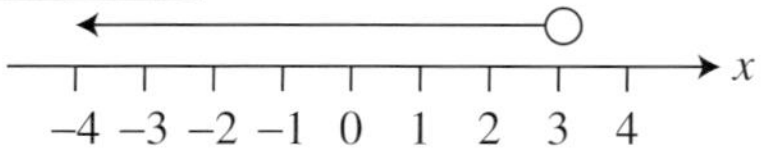

a Write down the inequality shown by this number line.
b Write down the largest integer x could be.

a All the values on the arrow are smaller than 3 so $x < 3$.
b The largest integer x could be is 2.

1 Copy and complete the following, using < or > in place of the boxes.

a 5 □ 8 **b** 7 □ 2 **c** $^{-}1$ □ 3
d 15 □ 6 **e** $^{-}7$ □ $^{-}9$ **f** $^{-}2$ □ 6

2 Represent these inequalities on a number line.

a $x > 2$ **b** $x < 4$

3 Write down the inequalities shown on these number lines.

a

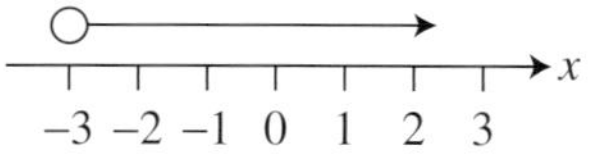

b

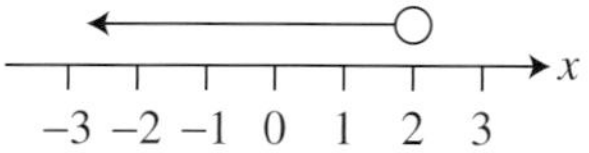

c

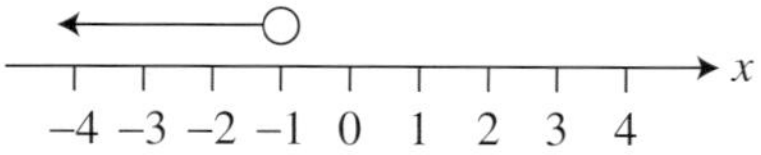

4 **a** What is the smallest integer that x could be in question **3a**?

b What is the largest integer that x could be in question **3b**?

c What is the largest integer that x could be in question **3c**?

5 What is the smallest negative integer that satisfies the inequality $x > {}^{-}4$?

9D Changing fractions to percentages

Example

There are 18 girls and 22 boys in a class.
Find the percentage of girls in this class.

18 + 22 = 40 students

$$\frac{18}{40} \xrightarrow{\div 2} \frac{9}{20} \xrightarrow{\times 5} \frac{45}{100}$$

$$\frac{18}{40} = \frac{9}{20} = \frac{45}{100} = 45\%$$

÷ 2 × 5

1 Copy and complete:

a $\frac{3}{5} = \frac{\square}{100} = \square\%$ **b** $\frac{11}{20} = \frac{\square}{100} = \square\%$ **c** $\frac{49}{50} = \frac{\square}{100} = \square\%$

d $\frac{6}{15} = \frac{\square}{5} = \frac{\square}{100} = \square\%$ **e** $\frac{26}{40} = \frac{\square}{20} = \frac{\square}{100} = \square\%$

2 Write as a percentage:

a $\frac{1}{5}$ **b** $\frac{3}{4}$ **c** $\frac{9}{10}$ **d** $\frac{17}{20}$ **e** $\frac{21}{25}$ **f** $\frac{33}{50}$

g $\frac{18}{75}$ **h** $\frac{39}{52}$ **i** $\frac{38}{40}$ **j** $\frac{33}{55}$ **k** $\frac{48}{60}$ **l** $\frac{111}{150}$

3 For each shape, find the **i** fraction shaded **ii** percentage shaded.

a

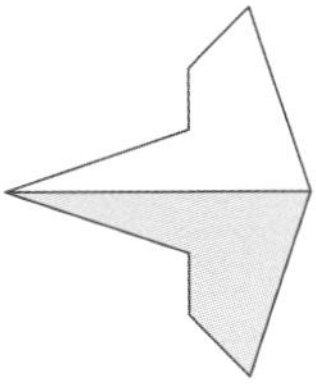

b

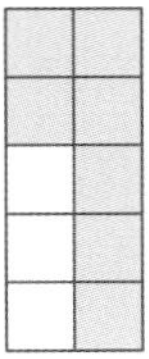

c

d

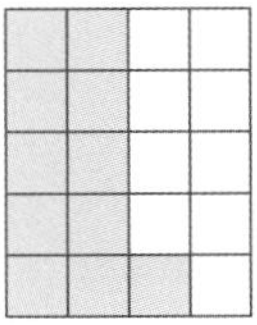

4 This table shows information about 40 people.

Find the percentage of:

a these people who have blue eyes

b these people who have dark hair

c those with fair hair who have brown eyes

d those with blue eyes who have fair hair.

	Fair hair	Dark hair
Blue eyes	12	7
Brown eyes	3	18

9J Adding and subtracting decimals

Example

Work out: **a** $2.05 + 3 + 1.78$ **b** $6.4 - 2.17$

a
$$\begin{array}{r} 2.05 \\ +\ 3 \\ +\ 1.78 \\ \hline 6.83 \\ \scriptstyle 1 \end{array}$$

b
$$\begin{array}{r} \scriptstyle 3\,1 \\ 6.\not{4}0 \\ -\ 2.17 \\ \hline 4.23 \end{array}$$

1 Work out:

a $4.3 + 2.4$ **b** $5.2 + 1.8$ **c** $6.5 + 2.7$ **d** $6 + 3.9$

e $2.3 + 7$ **f** $0.02 + 6.4$ **g** $3.98 + 4.6$ **h** $5.77 + 4.28$

2 Work out:

a $5 + 0.5 + 0.27$ **b** $2.3 + 9 + 1.03$ **c** $0.05 + 0.28 + 4$

d $20 + 1.9 + 0.22$ **e** $17.2 + 156 + 0.74$ **f** $0.002 + 86 + 0.96$

3 Find the total cost of a book for \$8.49, an album for \$15 and a pen for \$5.89.

4 Find the odd one out:

$3.487 + 5.963 + 2.09$	$4.9 + 3.077 + 3.553$	$8 + 0.998 + 2.532$

5 The times for the four runners in a 4×100 metre relay team were:

11.47 s	11.58 s	12.24 s	11.08 s

a Find their total time.

b The previous club record was 47.03 seconds.
By how much did they better the record?

6 The numbers in the squares are the sum of the numbers in the circles.
Find the missing numbers.

a

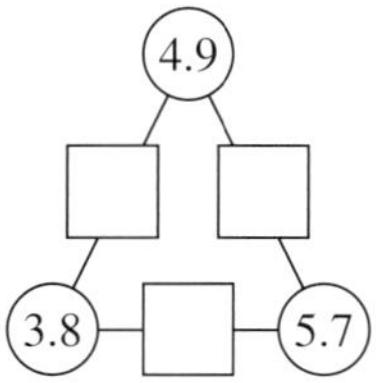

b

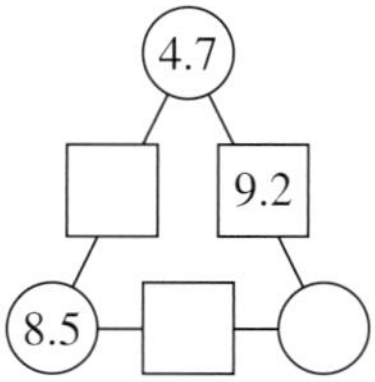

c

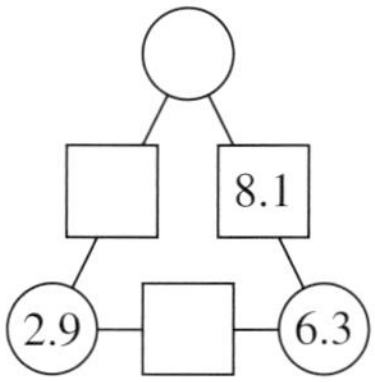

7 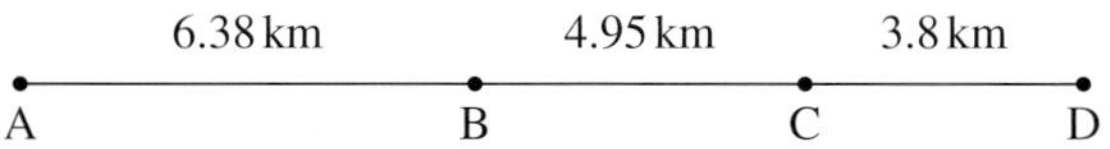

Find the distance between A and D.

8 Work out:

a $38.4 - 12$ **b** $9.2 - 2.8$ **c** $7 - 0.6$

d $15 - 2.3$ **e** $15.3 - 6.7$ **f** $4.7 - 2.08$

g $21 - 0.39$ **h** $12.68 - 4.004$ **i** $7.8 - 5.68$

j $80 - 8.47$ **k** $17.3 - 6.48$ **l** $20.3 - 5.998$

9 Find the odd one out.

$5.249 - 3.184$	$18.605 - 15.64$	$3.631 - 1.566$

10 Raju bought a book for \$9.35 and a pack of pens for \$7.89.
He paid with a \$20 bill.
How much change did he receive?

11 Helen and Anya took part in a long jump competition.
Helen jumped 6.45 metres and Anya jumped 5.87 metres.
How much further did Helen jump than Anya?

12 **a** By rounding each number to the nearest integer, estimate the answers to these calculations.

i $^{-}4.28 + 6.57$ **ii** $^{-}2.77 - {}^{-}3.8$ **iii** $^{-}1.72 - 3.98 - {}^{-}1.342$

b Now work out the exact answers and compare them to your estimates.

13 Find the missing numbers.

a
$$\begin{array}{r} 9.\square 3 \\ -\ \square.4\,5 \\ \hline 6.8\,8 \end{array}$$

b
$$\begin{array}{r} \square.4\,\square \\ -\ 5.\square\,2 \\ \hline 2.7\,4 \end{array}$$

c
$$\begin{array}{r} 4.2\,9\,\square \\ -\ \square.6\,\square\,7 \\ \hline 1.\square\,4\,6 \end{array}$$

14 Work out:

a $12.6 + {}^{-}6.35$ **b** $5.8 - {}^{-}4.88$

c $^{-}12.6 + 7.21$ **d** $5.2 + {}^{-}8.9$

e $8.4 - 10.2 + 9.65$ **f** $^{-}8.9 + 3.3 + 5.07$

g $^{-}4.9 + 8.14 + {}^{-}2.65$ **h** $^{-}5.8 + {}^{-}5.8 - {}^{-}5.8$

10C Summary statistics

Example

This frequency table shows the test marks of 20 students.

Mark	7	8	9	10
Frequency	4	9	5	2

a Calculate the mean mark.
b Find the modal test mark.
c Find the median test mark.
d Find the range of test marks.

---

a Mean $= \frac{(7 \times 4) + (8 \times 9) + (9 \times 5) + (10 \times 2)}{20}$

$= \frac{28 + 72 + 45 + 20}{20}$

$= \frac{165}{20}$

$= 8.25$

b Mode = test mark that occurs most often = 8

c Median $= \frac{20+1}{2}$ th value = 10.5th value = 8

d Range = largest value – smallest value
$= 10 - 7 = 3$

1 This table shows the number of pets owned by 20 people.

Number of pets	Frequency	Number of pets × frequency
0	5	$0 \times 5 = 0$
1	8	$1 \times 8 =$
2	6	
3	1	
Total		

a Copy and complete the table. Find the mean number of pets.

b Find the modal number of pets.

c Find the median number of pets.

d Find the range of the number of pets.

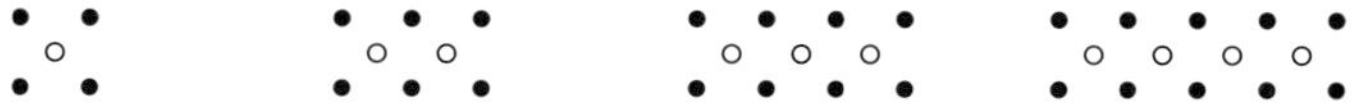

   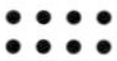   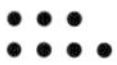 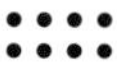    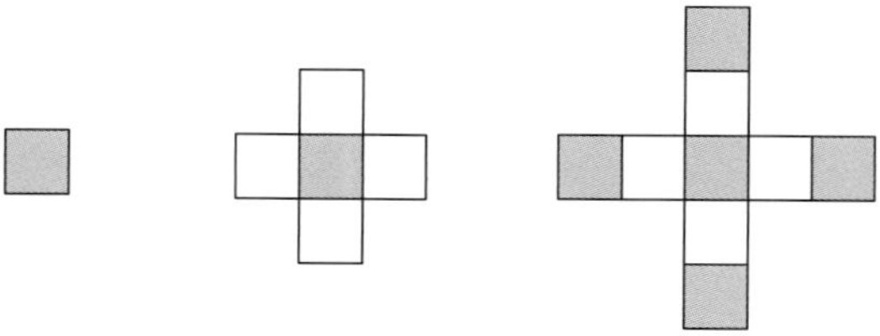

12C The *n*th term

Example

Find the nth term for the sequence 7, 8, 9, 10, 11, ...

First term is	$1+6$
Second term is	$2+6$
Third term is	$3+6$
Fourth term is	$4+6$
Fifth term is	$5+6$
nth term is	$n+6$

1 The position-to-term rule for a sequence is $n + 4$.

a Find the 20th term.

b Find the 100th term.

2 The position-to-term rule for a sequence is $n - 7$.

a Find the 10th term.

b Find the 50th term.

3 The position-to-term rule for a sequence is $4n$.

a Find the 40th term.

b One term has value 76. Which term is it?

4 Find the nth term of each of these sequences.

a 2, 3, 4, 5, 6, …

b 7, 8, 9, 10, 11, …

c 5, 6, 7, 8, 9, …

d $^-3, ^-2, ^-1, 0, 1$, …

e 4, 8, 12, 16, 20, …

f 6, 12, 18, 24, 30, …

g $^-2, ^-4, ^-6, ^-8, ^-10$, ...

h $^-7, ^-14, ^-21, ^-28, ^-35$, …

5 The nth term of a sequence is $n - 5$.
How many negative terms are there in the sequence?

6 The position-to-term rule for a sequence is $7 - 3n$.
Write down the first five terms of this sequence.

7 The position-to-term rule for a sequence is $5n - 2$.

a Find the 40th term.

b One term has value 83. Which term is it?

12F Horizontal and vertical lines

Example

Draw the graph of $y = 2$.

Every point on the line $y = 2$ will have a y-coordinate of 2.
Some of these points are: (3, 2), (1, 2), ($^{-}3$, 2), (2, 2).
Plot the points on a pair of axes and join with a straight line.

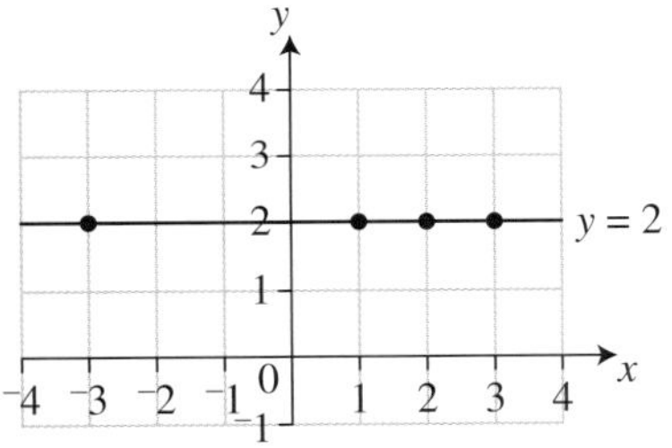

1 Plot the points (3, 4), (1, 4), ($^{-}3$, 4), (2, 4) and ($^{-}1$, 4) on a pair of axes.
What is the equation of the straight line that passes through these five points?

2 Plot the points ($^{-}3$, 5), ($^{-}3$, $^{-}3$), ($^{-}3$, 1), ($^{-}3$, $^{-}5$) and ($^{-}3$, 4) on a pair of axes.
What is the equation of the straight line that passes through these five points?

3 Write down the equations of the lines A, B, C, D, E and F.

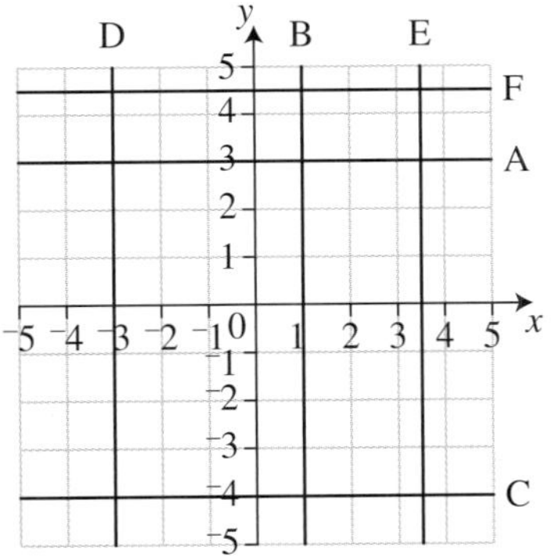

4 For each set of coordinates, write down an equation for the line that passes through all of them.

a ($^{-}2$, 4), ($^{-}2$, $^{-}3$), ($^{-}2$, 8), ($^{-}2$, $^{-}5$), ($^{-}2$, $^{-}7$)

b (3, 3), ($^{-}3$, $^{-}3$), (5, 5), (0, 0), ($^{-}2$, $^{-}2$)

c (2, 6), (3, 9), (1, 3), (0, 0), (5, 15)

d (1, 7), (2, 12), (3, 17), (4, 22), (10, 52)

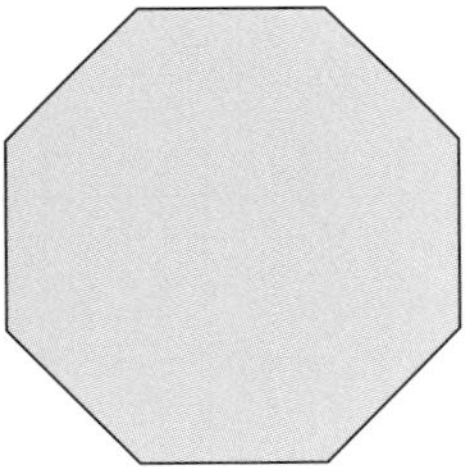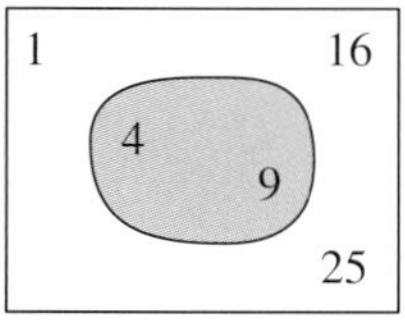

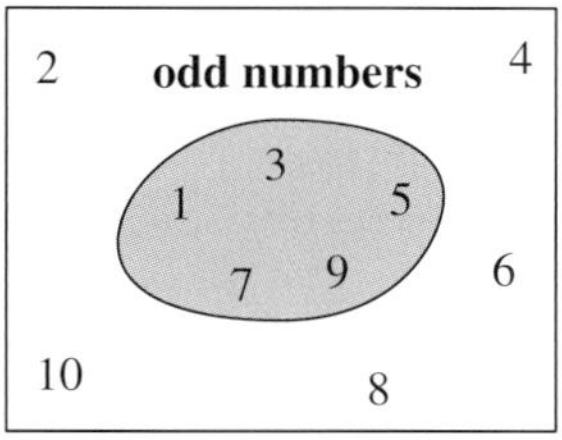

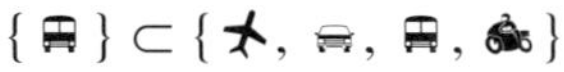

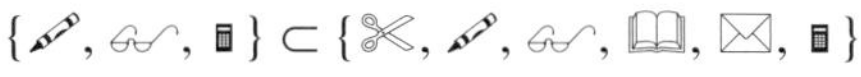

OXFORD
UNIVERSITY PRESS

ASPIRE
SUCCEED
PROGRESS

Cambridge
Lower Secondary
Complete Mathematics 7

Sue Pemberton

Second Edition

HOMEWORK BOOK

Oxford excellence for Cambridge Lower Secondary

OXFORD

OXFORD
UNIVERSITY PRESS

Great Clarendon Street, Oxford, OX2 6DP, United Kingdom

Oxford University Press is a department of the University of Oxford. It furthers the University's objective of excellence in research, scholarship, and education by publishing worldwide. Oxford is a registered trade mark of Oxford University Press in the UK and in certain other countries

© Oxford University Press 2021

The moral rights of the author have been asserted

First published in 2021

All rights reserved. No part of this publication may be reproduced, stored in a retrieval system, or transmitted, in any form or by any means, without the prior permission in writing of Oxford University Press, or as expressly permitted by law, by licence or under terms agreed with the appropriate reprographics rights organization. Enquiries concerning reproduction outside the scope of the above should be sent to the Rights Department, Oxford University Press, at the address above.

You must not circulate this work in any other form and you must impose this same condition on any acquirer

British Library Cataloguing in Publication Data

Data available

978-1-38-201873-9

10 9 8 7 6 5 4 3 2 1

Paper used in the production of this book is a natural, recyclable product made from wood grown in sustainable forests. The manufacturing process conforms to the environmental regulations of the country of origin.

Printed in the UK by Bell and Bain Ltd, Glasgow

Acknowledgements

The publisher and authors would like to thank the following for permission to use photographs and other copyright material:

Cover: Eugene Mymrin/Getty Images.

All artwork by Integra Software Services.

Every effort has been made to contact copyright holders of material reproduced in this book. Any omissions will be rectified in subsequent printings if notice is given to the publisher.

MIX
Paper from responsible sources
FSC www.fsc.org FSC® C007785

Contents

1A Adding and subtracting negative numbers

Example

Work out: **a** $6 + {}^{-}2$ **b** ${}^{-}7 - {}^{-}3$

a $6 + {}^{-}2 = 6 - 2 = 4$ **b** ${}^{-}7 - {}^{-}3 = {}^{-}7 + 3 = {}^{-}4$

1 Copy and complete these sequences.

a 5, 3, 1, $^{-}1$, □, □, □ **b** 30, 23, 16, 9, □, □, □

c $^{-}36$, $^{-}31$, $^{-}26$, $^{-}21$, □, □, □

2 Work out:

a $6 + {}^{-}4$ **b** $8 + {}^{-}7$ **c** $5 + {}^{-}5$ **d** $8 + {}^{-}10$

e $9 + {}^{-}3$ **f** $14 + {}^{-}8$ **g** $6 + {}^{-}8$ **h** $2 + {}^{-}9$

i ${}^{-}6 + {}^{-}2$ **j** ${}^{-}1 + {}^{-}7$ **k** ${}^{-}3 + {}^{-}6$ **l** ${}^{-}12 + {}^{-}15$

m ${}^{-}8 + {}^{-}5$ **n** ${}^{-}6 + {}^{-}11$ **o** ${}^{-}4 + {}^{-}9$ **p** ${}^{-}6 + {}^{-}6$

3 Work out:

a $6 - {}^{-}4$ **b** $9 - {}^{-}2$ **c** $5 - {}^{-}8$ **d** $1 - {}^{-}1$

e ${}^{-}4 - {}^{-}6$ **f** ${}^{-}8 - {}^{-}2$ **g** ${}^{-}5 - {}^{-}5$ **h** ${}^{-}2 - {}^{-}5$

i ${}^{-}14 - {}^{-}8$ **j** ${}^{-}13 - {}^{-}11$ **k** ${}^{-}9 - {}^{-}32$ **l** ${}^{-}46 - {}^{-}18$

4 Work out:

a ${}^{-}4 + {}^{-}3 + 8$ **b** ${}^{-}7 - {}^{-}5 + {}^{-}3$ **c** $8 + {}^{-}5 - {}^{-}7$

d ${}^{-}1 + {}^{-}6 + {}^{-}9$ **e** $9 - {}^{-}7 + {}^{-}4$ **f** $29 - {}^{-}11 + 9$

g ${}^{-}6 + {}^{-}6 - {}^{-}6$ **h** $11 - {}^{-}22 + {}^{-}33$ **i** ${}^{-}2 - {}^{-}6 + {}^{-}9$

5 Copy and complete:

a $7 - \square = {}^{-}2$ **b** $\square + 7 = {}^{-}23$ **c** $15 + \square = 6$

d $\square + {}^{-}11 = {}^{-}16$ **e** $12 + \square = {}^{-}14$ **f** $\square + {}^{-}26 = {}^{-}2$

6 Work out: $15 + {}^{-}8 - 2 + {}^{-}6$

7 Write down five different numbers that add together to give the number $^{-}3$.

8 Numbers in squares = the sum of numbers in circles. Find the missing numbers.

a

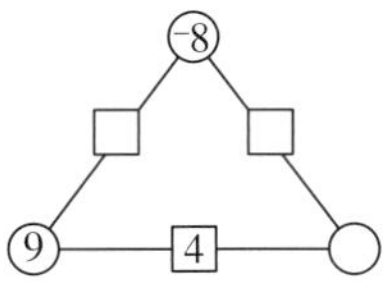

b

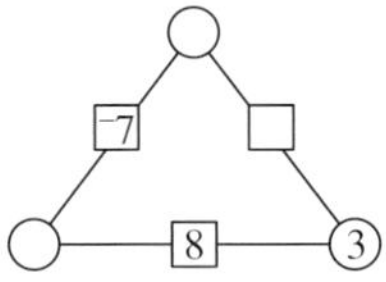

c

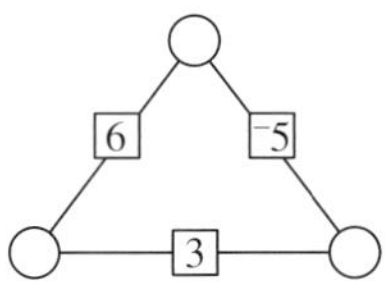

1B Multiplying and dividing negative numbers

Example

Work out: **a** $4 \times {}^{-}3$ **b** ${}^{-}40 \div 5$

a $4 \times {}^{-}3 = {}^{-}12$ **b** ${}^{-}40 \div 5 = {}^{-}8$

1 Work out:

a $6 \times {}^{-}4$ **b** $8 \times {}^{-}7$ **c** $5 \times {}^{-}5$ **d** $8 \times {}^{-}10$

e $9 \times {}^{-}3$ **f** $14 \times {}^{-}8$ **g** $6 \times {}^{-}8$ **h** $2 \times {}^{-}9$

i ${}^{-}4 \times 8$ **j** ${}^{-}11 \times 5$ **k** ${}^{-}9 \times 3$ **l** ${}^{-}16 \times 5$

2 Work out:

a $4 \times {}^{-}3 \times 2$ **b** ${}^{-}2 \times 5 \times 3$ **c** $4 \times {}^{-}1 \times 3$

d ${}^{-}1 \times 6 \times 9$ **e** $2 \times {}^{-}7 \times 4$ **f** $5 \times {}^{-}11 \times 2$

3 Work out:

$92 \times {}^{-}37 \times 43 \times 0 \times 17$

4 Find the missing numbers.

a ${}^{-}5 \times \square = {}^{-}20$ **b** $\square \times 6 = {}^{-}72$

5 Work out:

a $8 \div {}^{-}4$ **b** $15 \div {}^{-}3$ **c** $18 \div {}^{-}2$ **d** $20 \div {}^{-}10$

e $9 \div {}^{-}3$ **f** $40 \div {}^{-}8$ **g** $64 \div {}^{-}8$ **h** $27 \div {}^{-}9$

i ${}^{-}48 \div 8$ **j** ${}^{-}35 \div 5$ **k** ${}^{-}42 \div 3$ **l** ${}^{-}75 \div 5$

6 Work out:

a $\frac{{}^{-}16}{4}$ **b** $\frac{{}^{-}24}{3}$ **c** $\frac{8}{{}^{-}2}$ **d** $\frac{75}{{}^{-}15}$

7 Work out:

a $\frac{3 \times {}^{-}4}{4}$ **b** $\frac{8 \times {}^{-}3}{{}^{-}5 + 7}$ **c** $\frac{16}{{}^{-}2} + \frac{{}^{-}20}{2}$ **d** ${}^{-}8 - \frac{{}^{-}18}{3}$

e $\frac{{}^{-}2 + {}^{-}8}{5}$ **f** $\frac{45}{{}^{-}3} \div \frac{27}{9}$ **g** $\frac{2 - {}^{-}4}{16 \div 8}$ **h** ${}^{-}5 + \frac{{}^{-}10}{5} + {}^{-}8$

1C Estimation

Example

Estimate the result of 794 √ 18.

794 is 800 (to nearest 100)

18 is 20 (to nearest 10)

So, 794 √ 18 is approximately $800 \div 20 = 40$

1 Make good estimates for these calculations.

a $59 + 302 + 74$ **b** 49×52

c $611 - 198$ **d** 819 √ 198

e $222 + 912 - 304$ **f** $5132 - 783$

g $\frac{809 - 191}{121 + 205}$ **h** $\frac{94 \times 63}{22}$

2 The distance around a cycle track is 3.88 km. A cyclist completes 21 laps of the track. Estimate how far the cyclist travels in total.

3 There are 5800 spectators at a cricket match. Each spectator pays $12 for a ticket. Estimate the amount of money received from ticket sales.

4 Copy and complete the table. For each question, make a sensible guess and then use your calculator.

Problem	Guess	Calculation
$^{-}30 \times 11$		
$^{-}431 - 294$		
$^{-}815 \div 18$		
$^{-}513 + 187 - {}^{-}922$		
$^{-}682 \times 71$		

5 There are 500 sheets of paper in a ream. A ream is about 5.2 cm thick. Estimate the thickness of one sheet of paper.

1D Order of operations

Example

Work out $18 - (5 - 2) \times 4$

$18 - (5 - 2) \times 4 = 18 - 3 \times 4$ **B**rackets first, then

$= 18 - 12$ **M**ultiplication

$= 6$

1 Work out:

a $9 - 2 \times 3$ **b** $6 + 5 \times 4$ **c** $24 \div 6 - 2$

d $4 + 18 \div 2$ **e** $11 + 2 \times 9$ **f** $30 - 16 \div 4$

g $10 - 36 \times 2$ **h** $15 - 4 \times 7$ **i** $2 - 52 \div 4$

j $1 + 2 \times 3 + 4$ **k** $5 + 3 \times 6 - 9$ **l** $7 + 3 \times 2 - 4$

m $7 - 36 \div 9 + 2$ **n** $8 + 20 \div 5 - 3$ **o** $4 \times 5 + 6 \times 7$

p $3 \times 4 + 15 \div 3$ **q** $10 \div 2 + 3 \times 4$ **r** $18 \div 9 - 20 \div 4$

2 Work out:

a $2 \times (3 + 4)$ **b** $5 + (8 \div 2)$ **c** $3 \times (18 \div 2)$

d $40 \div (12 - 8)$ **e** $2 \times (8 - 5) \times 4$ **f** $5 - (82 - 50)$

g $(12 + 2) \times (13 + 7)$ **h** $(8 + 4) \div (7 - 5)$ **i** $8 \times (9 + 3) \times 5$

3 Work out:

a $5 + 2 \times 6$ **b** $2 - 12 \div 4$ **c** $6 + 5^2 \times 2$

d $4^3 + 6 \times {}^{-}3$ **e** $10^2 \times (6 - 10)$ **f** ${}^{-}2 \times {}^{-}3 + 4$

g $48 \div {}^{-}2 + 7 \times 2$ **h** $10 \div {}^{-}5 - {}^{-}2$ **i** ${}^{-}5 + 2^3 \times 3^2 - 17$

4 Copy these and insert brackets to make the statements correct.

a $5 \times 6 + 7 = 65$ **b** $20 - 12 \div 4 = 2$

c $12 \times 9 - 8 \times 2 = 24$ **d** $7 \times 2 - 10 \div 2 = 2$

e $14 - 10 \div 2 = 2$ **f** $9 + 6 \times 8 - 5 = 45$

1E Multiples and factors

Example

Find **a** the HCF of 12 and 30
b the LCM of 3 and 4.

a Factors of 12 = **1**, **2**, **3**, 4, **6**, 12
Factors of 30 = **1**, **2**, **3**, 5, **6**, 10, 15, 30
HCF (highest common factor) = 6

Common factors are 1, 2, 3, 6.

b Multiples of 3 = 3, 6, 9, **12**, 15, 18, 21, **24**, …
Multiples of 4 = 4, 8, **12**, 16, 20, **24**, 28, …
LCM (lowest common multiple) = 12

Common multiples are 12, 24, ...

1 Write the first five multiples of:

a 4 **b** 7 **c** 10 **d** 12 **e** 17 **f** 25

2 Write the first three numbers that are multiples of both:

a 3 and 4 **b** 4 and 7 **c** 5 and 9 **d** 6 and 7

3 Write the first three numbers that are multiples of:

a 2, 3 and 5 **b** 4, 5 and 6 **c** 2, 5 and 9

4 Write all the factors of:

a 7 **b** 10 **c** 16 **d** 24 **e** 56 **f** 40
g 32 **h** 41 **i** 63 **j** 75 **k** 60 **l** 64

5 Find the HCF of:

a 16 and 20 **b** 20 and 28 **c** 30 and 36 **d** 24 and 40
e 40 and 48 **f** 48 and 54 **g** 24 and 48 **h** 28 and 54
i 45 and 60 **j** 24 and 36 **k** 75 and 100 **l** 60 and 84
m 75 and 90 **n** 100 and 95 **o** 32 and 48 **p** 28 and 42

6 Find the HCF of:

a 15, 20 and 30 **b** 12, 15 and 21 **c** 12, 20 and 40
d 6, 12 and 15 **e** 28, 42 and 70 **f** 34, 68 and 85

7 Find the LCM of:

a 2 and 6	**b** 2 and 10	**c** 3 and 12	**d** 3 and 18
e 12 and 4	**f** 20 and 4	**g** 15 and 5	**h** 25 and 5
i 5 and 6	**j** 7 and 8	**k** 4 and 7	**l** 3 and 10
m 9 and 11	**n** 8 and 9	**o** 7 and 5	**p** 9 and 4

8 Find the LCM of:

a 3, 4 and 6	**b** 5, 8 and 12	**c** 5, 6 and 7
d 5, 10 and 15	**e** 4, 7 and 8	**f** 3, 15 and 18

9 A light flashes every 12 minutes. A second light flashes every 28 minutes. Both lights flash at 9 am. What will be the time when they next flash together?

1F Divisibility tests

Example

A number is divisible by 3 if the sum of its digits is divisible by 3.

a Is 348 divisible by 3? **b** Is 1927 divisible by 3?

a $3 + 4 + 8 = 15$
15 is divisible by 3
so 348 is divisible by 3

b $1 + 9 + 2 + 7 = 19$
19 is not divisible by 3 so
1927 is not divisible by 3

Use divisibility tests to answer these questions.

1 Which of these numbers are divisible by 3?

a 51 **b** 82 **c** 104 **d** 117
e 162 **f** 451 **g** 845 **h** 6432

2 Which of these numbers are divisible by 5?

a 87 **b** 45 **c** 236 **d** 439
e 545 **f** 1068 **g** 6534 **h** 9875

3 Which of these numbers are divisible by 2?

a 77 **b** 98 **c** 114 **d** 237
e 86 **f** 779 **g** 5243 **h** 6766

4 A number is divisible by 4 if the number formed from the last two digits is divisible by 4. Which of these numbers are divisible by 4?

a 308 **b** 244 **c** 555 **d** 236
e 783 **f** 6520 **g** 7654 **h** 9888

5 A number is divisible by 9 if the sum of its digits is divisible by 9. Which of these numbers are divisible by 9?

a 126 **b** 415 **c** 368 **d** 675
e 2377 **f** 6666 **g** 9162 **h** 7557

6 A number is divisible by 6 if it is an even number **and** the sum of its digits is divisible by 3. Which of these numbers are divisible by 6?

a 84 **b** 426 **c** 252 **d** 441
e 783 **f** 722 **g** 6432 **h** 8116

7 How can you test whether a 3-digit number is divisible by 11?

1G–1I Square and cube roots

Example

Work out $\sqrt{81} + \sqrt{49}$

$\sqrt{81} + \sqrt{49} = 9 + 7 = 16$

1 Write down the value of:

a $\sqrt{25}$ **b** $\sqrt{81}$ **c** $\sqrt{16}$ **d** $\sqrt{289}$

2 Work out the value of:

a 2^2 **b** 3^2 **c** 7^2 **d** 15^2

e $(^-2)^2$ **f** $(^-3)^2$ **g** $(^-7)^2$ **h** $(^-15)^2$

3 Work out:

a $\sqrt{36}$ **b** $\sqrt{64}$ **c** $\sqrt{100}$ **d** $\sqrt{144}$

e $\sqrt{81} + \sqrt{4}$ **f** $\sqrt{49} - \sqrt{16}$ **g** $\sqrt{4} \times \sqrt{9}$ **h** $\sqrt{100} \surd \sqrt{4}$

i $\sqrt{9 + 16}$ **j** $\sqrt{9} + \sqrt{16}$ **k** $\sqrt{100 - 36}$ **l** $\sqrt{100} - \sqrt{36}$

m $\sqrt{4 \times 25}$ **n** $\sqrt{4} \times \sqrt{25}$ **o** $\sqrt{36 \surd 4}$ **p** $\sqrt{36} \surd \sqrt{4}$

4 Write down the lengths of the sides of each of these squares.

a

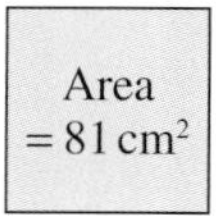

b

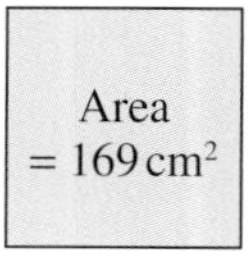

5 Write down the value of:

a $\sqrt[3]{27}$ **b** $\sqrt[3]{8}$ **c** $\sqrt[3]{^-64}$ **d** $\sqrt[3]{^-1000}$

6 Use a calculator to work out:

a 1.2^3 **b** 2.5^3 **c** $(^-6.1)^3$ **d** $(^-0.3)^3$

e $\sqrt[3]{74.088}$ **f** $\sqrt[3]{0.343}$ **g** $\sqrt[3]{4096}$ **h** $\sqrt[3]{13.824}$

7 Use a calculator to find the value of x for each of these cubes.

a

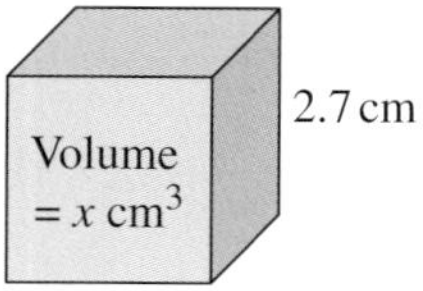

b

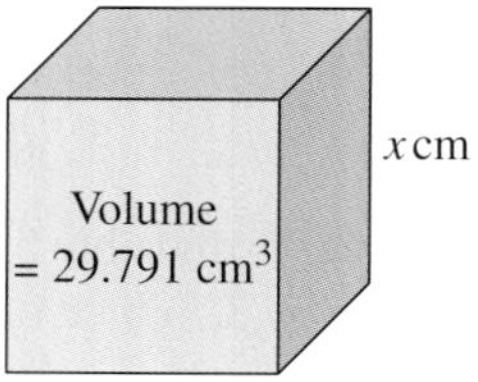

8 Work out the value of:

a $\sqrt{\frac{9}{49}}$ **b** $\sqrt{\frac{16}{25}}$ **c** $\sqrt{0.36}$ **d** $\sqrt{0.09}$

e $\sqrt[3]{\frac{8}{27}}$ **f** $\sqrt[3]{\frac{64}{125}}$ **g** $\sqrt[3]{\frac{1}{64}}$ **h** $\sqrt[3]{0.008}$

2A Algebraic expressions

Example

A chocolate costs c cents and a toffee costs t cents.
Write an expression for the total cost of 5 chocolates and 3 toffees.

Cost of 5 chocolates $= 5 \times c = 5c$
Cost of 3 toffees $= 3 \times t = 3t$
Total cost $= (5c + 3t)$ cents

1 A piece of string is x cm long. I cut off a piece 5 cm long.
How much string remains?

2 A piece of rope is 15 m long. I cut off a piece y m long.
How much rope remains?

3 A brick has a mass of m kg.
What is the total mass of 8 bricks?

4 A bus can carry p passengers.
How many passengers are on the bus if there are 4 empty seats?

5 A pencil costs p cents and a ruler costs r cents.
Write an expression for the total cost of 5 pencils and 7 rulers.

6 A banana costs b cents and a pineapple costs p cents.
Write an expression for the total cost of 8 bananas and 2 pineapples.

7 I buy 2 books costing \$$x$ each.
I pay for the books with a \$20 note.
How much change do I receive from the \$20 note?

8 Debbie gives b biscuits to each of her 5 friends.
She then gives 1 more biscuit to each of her 5 friends.
How many biscuits has she given to her friends?

9 A farmer puts c cows and g goats into each of 8 fields.
The next day the farmer puts 3 more cows into each of the 8 fields.
Write an expression for the total number of animals in the fields.

2B–2C Using expressions

Example

Write an expression for:

a the area of this rectangle

b the perimeter of this rectangle.

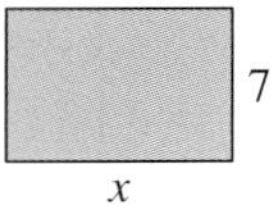

---

a Area = base × height = $x \times 7 = 7x$

b Perimeter = total distance around the edge

$= x + 7 + x + 7$

$= 2x + 14$

1 Write an expression for the area of each rectangle.

a

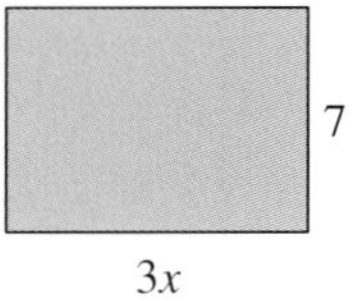

b

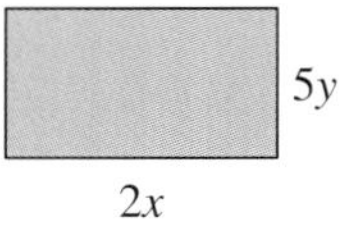

c

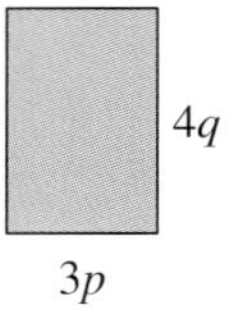

2 Write an expression for the perimeter of each shape.

a

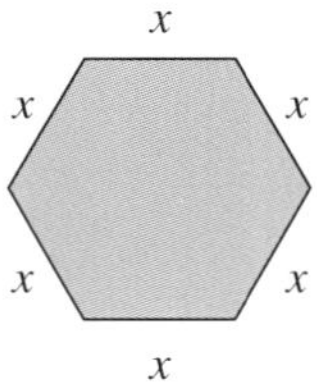

b

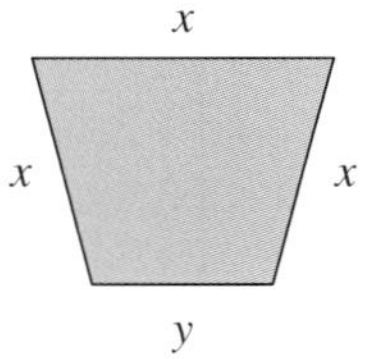

c

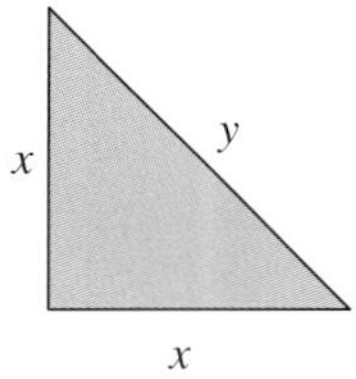

3 How many days are there in:

a 1 week **b** 4 weeks **c** x weeks **d** $2x$ weeks?

4 Write an expression for the shaded area.

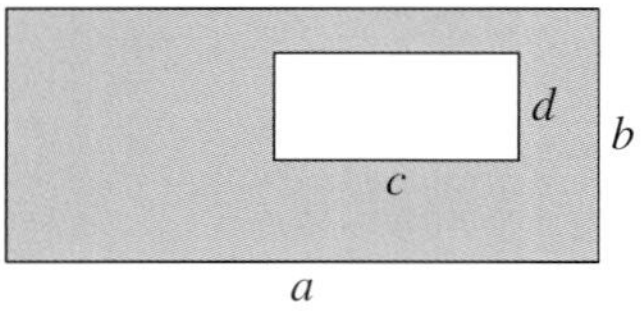

5 Karl is x years old. How old will he be in y years' time?

6 Khadija had \$36 and she spent \$$x$.
How much money does she have left?

7 Haroon has \$$x$. He shares it equally between his 5 friends.
How much does each friend receive?

8 Zara buys x shirts at \$12 each and y skirts at \$19 each.
How much does she spend altogether?

2D–2E Simplifying expressions and equations

Example

Simplify $7a + 5b - 3c + 2a - 2c - 8b$

$$7a + 5b - 3c + 2a - 2c - 8b = 7a + 2a + 5b - 8b - 3c - 2c$$

Group together like terms.

$$= 9a - 3b - 5c$$

Simplify.

1 Simplify:

a $5x + 2y + 3x + 4y$ **b** $8f + 3g + 5f + 2g$ **c** $5y + 4 + 3y + 6$

d $6a + 5b - 2a - 3b$ **e** $9q + 8 - q - 3$ **f** $5x - 2y + 3x + 6y$

g $5x - 10y + 2x + 3y$ **h** $8c + 12d - 9d + 2c$ **i** $^{-}5x - y + 8x - 2y$

j $^{-}3a + 5b - 8b - a$

2 Simplify $6x + 5y - 3z + 7 + 4y - 15 - 18z - y + 25z$

3 Sort these cards into pairs of equivalent expressions.

$2a + 3a + 4b$ | $5 \times b \times a$ | $^{-}2a - 3a + 4b$

$2ab + 5$ | $4ab + 7 - 2ab - 2$

$2ab + 3ba$ | $7b + 5a - 3b$ | $5b + a - b - 6a$

4 Copy and complete:

a $5x + \square - 3x + 2y = 2x + 8y$ **b** $\square - 3m - 2n + m = 5n - 2m$

c $7a - 3b - \square - \square = {}^{-}2a - 4b$

5 Find the missing expressions or numbers.

a $5x + 4 - \square - 4x = x$ **b** $x + 2 + 2x - 5 + \square = x$

c $5 - 2x + 3 + 4x - \square = x$

6 Find an expression for the perimeter of this shape. Write your answer in its simplest form.

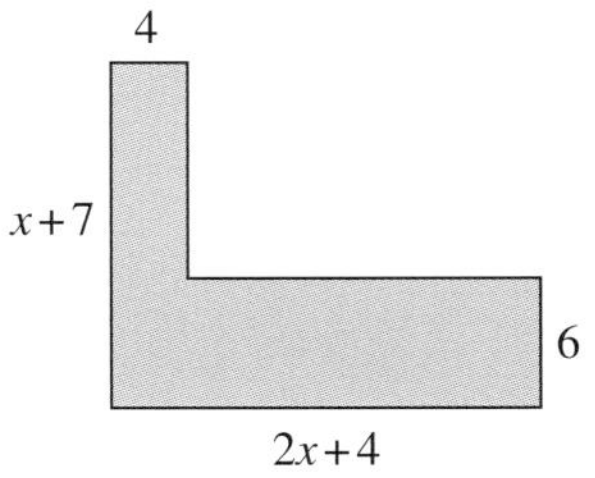

2F Expanding brackets

Example

Expand the brackets: **a** $5(2x+4)$ **b** $^{-}3(2x-7)$

a $5(2x+4) = 10x+20$

b $^{-}3(2x-7) = {}^{-}6x+21$

1 Expand the brackets.

a $3(x+2)$	**b** $4(y-5)$	**c** $5(8+a)$
d $6(3-p)$	**e** $2(x+y)$	**f** $3(a-b)$
g $8(m-n)$	**h** $7(p+q)$	**i** $6(2x+1)$
j $5(3y-2)$	**k** $4(6-5y)$	**l** $2(3v-4)$
m $3(2x+3y)$	**n** $4(6x-5y)$	**o** $9(4a+5b)$
p $8(3p-4q)$	**q** $^{-}2(x+2)$	**r** $^{-}4(y-1)$
s $^{-}3(4y+7)$	**t** $^{-}2(6-5y)$	

2 Expand the brackets.

a $4(2a+3b-5)$	**b** $3(5x-2y+z)$	**c** $6(1+2x+3y)$
d $2(5p-3+2q)$	**e** $7(3f+2g-5h)$	**f** $10(x-2y+3z)$
g $^{-}3(2x+y-4)$	**h** $^{-}2(a-3b+7)$	**i** $^{-}7(3p-q+4r)$

3 Expand the brackets.

a $\frac{1}{2}(4x+6)$	**b** $\frac{1}{2}(8y-10)$	**c** $\frac{1}{3}(6x-9)$
d $\frac{1}{5}(20x-15)$	**e** $\frac{1}{4}(28x+4)$	**f** $\frac{1}{8}(16-40x)$

4 Copy and complete:

a $3(2x+\square) = 6x+15$	**b** $4(3y-\square) = 12y-8$
c $8(6x-\square) = 48x-56$	**d** $5(\square-2y) = 25-10y$
e $6(\square x+3) = 12x+18$	**f** $\square(7x+2) = 28x+8$
g $\square(5y-4) = {}^{-}15y+12$	**h** $^{-}8(\square x+5) = {}^{-}16x-40$

2G–2H Expanding and simplifying

Example

Simplify: **a** $3(5x + 6) + 2(3x + 4)$
b $9(3y - 4) - 2(7y + 2)$

a $3(5x + 6) + 2(3x + 4) = 15x + 18 + 6x + 8$
$= 21x + 26$

b $9(3y - 4) - 2(7y + 2) = 27y - 36 - 14y - 4 = 13y - 40$

1 Simplify:

a $2(x + 3) + 3(x + 5)$ **b** $5(x + 2) + 4(x + 8)$ **c** $3(y + 4) + 7(y + 7)$

d $6(x - 5) + 3(x + 6)$ **e** $3(x + 4) + 2(x - 5)$ **f** $2(3y + 1) + 4(2y + 5)$

g $3(5x + 6) + 5(3x + 2)$ **h** $2(3x + 4) - 3(x + 2)$ **i** $4(2y - 1) + 3(2y - 5)$

j $5(x + 4) - 2(x - 3)$ **k** $3(5 - 2x) + 4(2x - 1)$ **l** $8(4x - 5) - 3(8 - 5x)$

m $2 + 3(x + 2)$ **n** $7 + 3(x + 5)$ **o** $14 + 2(3x - 5) + 5x$

p $8 - 5(x + 2)$ **q** $6x - (2 + x)$ **r** $4x - (2x - 5)$

2 **A** $3x + 4$ **B** $2x + 1$ **C** $x - 5$

Use the expressions above in the following, and then simplify:

a $3\mathbf{A} + 2\mathbf{B}$ **b** $3\mathbf{B} - 2\mathbf{C}$ **c** $5 + 2\mathbf{A}$ **d** $2\mathbf{A} + \mathbf{B} - 3\mathbf{C}$

3 Write an expression for the area of this rectangle.

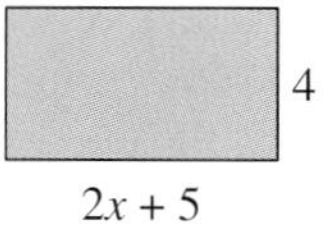

4 Find the area and perimeter of this shape.

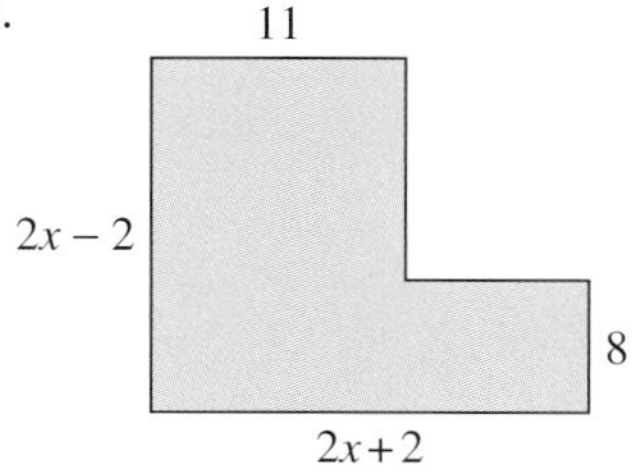

5 Expand and simplify:

a $\frac{1}{2}(10x + 8) + \frac{1}{3}(6x + 18)$ **b** $\frac{1}{4}(32x - 8) + \frac{1}{5}(15x + 20)$

6 Copy and complete: $5(x + \square) + \square(x + 3) = 7x + 21$

3A Polygons

Example

Name this polygon.

The polygon has 7 sides so it is a heptagon.

1 Name each polygon.

a 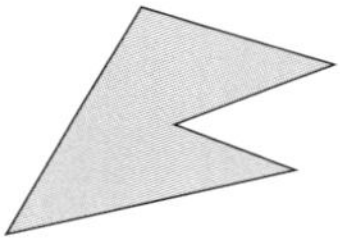

b 

c 

2 These polygons are regular. Name each polygon and write down the order of rotational symmetry and the number of lines of symmetry.

a 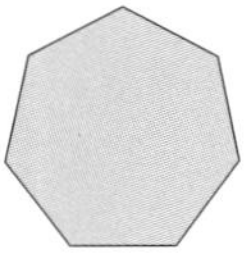

b 

c 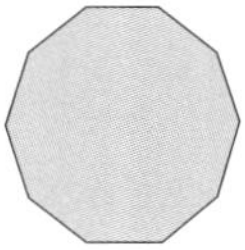

d 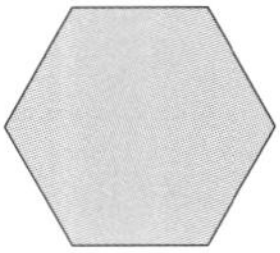

3 In the student book you found that:

- all of the angles in a regular pentagon are 108°
- all of the angles in a regular hexagon are 120°
- all of the angles in a regular octagon are 135°.

a Explain why it is possible to make this tiling pattern (with no gaps) using regular hexagons.

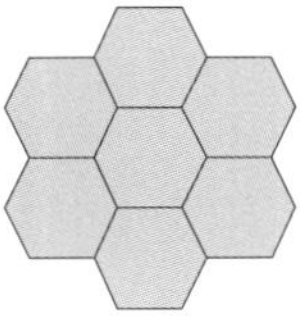

b Explain why you cannot make a tiling pattern (with no gaps) using regular pentagons.

c Can you make a tiling pattern (with no gaps) using squares and regular octagons? Explain your answer.

3B Congruency

Example

Draw two more triangles that are congruent to these triangles.

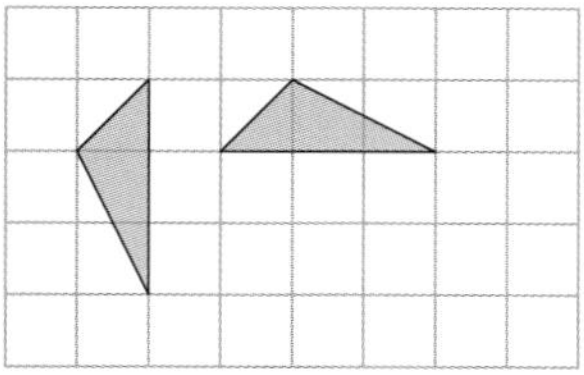

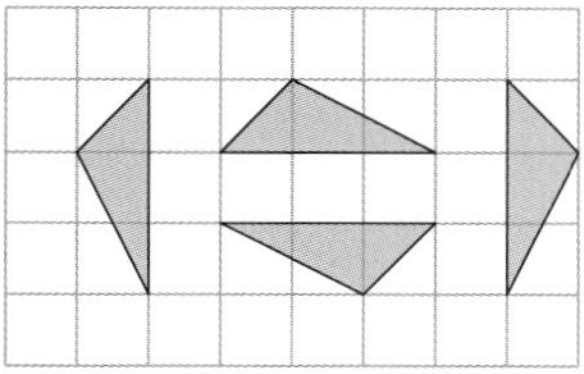

1 Draw two more quadrilaterals that are congruent to these quadrilaterals.

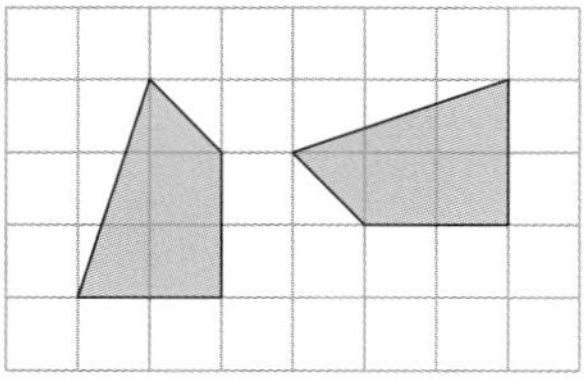

2

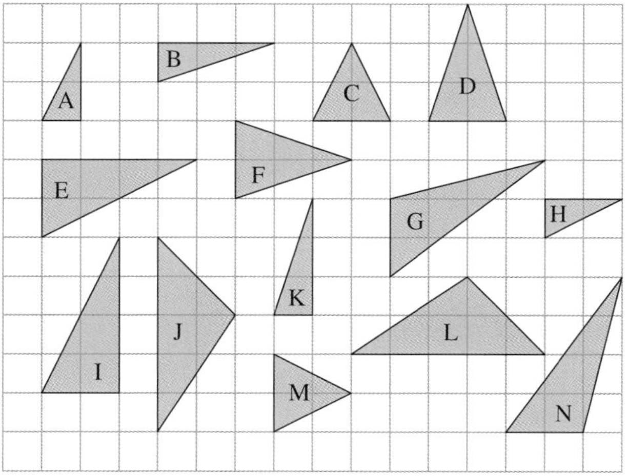

Find pairs of congruent triangles.

3 These two triangles are congruent. ABC ≡ PQR

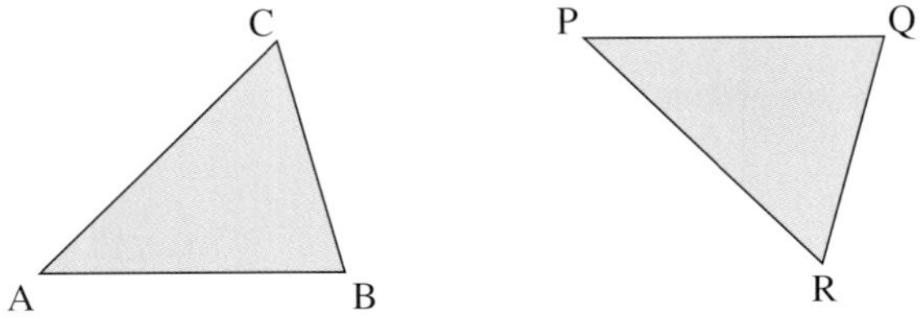

Copy and complete these mappings.

a $\hat{A} \rightarrow \square$ **b** $\hat{B} \rightarrow \square$ **c** $\hat{C} \rightarrow \square$

d AB $\rightarrow \square$ **e** BC $\rightarrow \square$ **f** AC $\rightarrow \square$

4 These two triangles are congruent. DEF ≡ XYZ

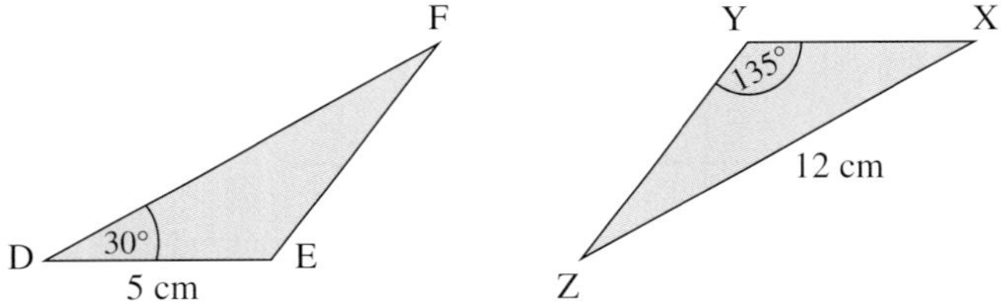

Use the information given in the diagrams to answer these questions.

a What are the lengths of XY and DF?

b What is the size of: **i** $Y\hat{X}Z$ **ii** $D\hat{E}F$

c Which angle of DEF is equal to $Y\hat{Z}X$? What is the size of this angle?

d Find a side that is the same length as ZY.

5

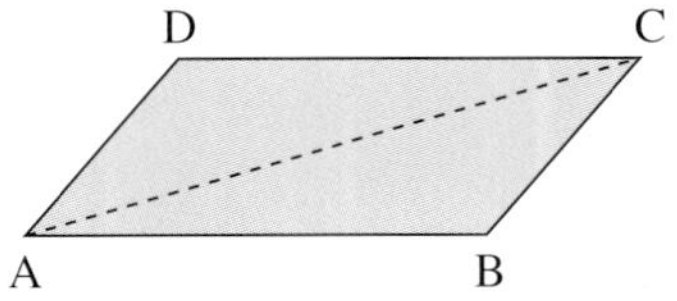

ABCD is a parallelogram.

Explain why triangles ABC and CDA are congruent.

3C Parts of a circle

Example

Copy and complete the following statement.
The radius of a circle is always . . . the length of the diameter of the circle.

The radius of a circle is always half the length of the diameter of the circle.

1 For each mathematical term, choose the card with its correct definition.

a circumference **b** chord **c** diameter **d** tangent

e arc **f** sector **g** segment **h** radius

A: A straight line that passes through the centre of a circle and whose endpoints lie on the circle

B: A straight line that intersects a circle at just one point

C: The region bounded by a chord of a circle and an arc of the circle

D: A portion of the circumference of a circle

E: A straight line whose endpoints lie on a circle

F: The region bounded by two radii of a circle and an arc of the circle

G: The distance around a circle

H: The distance from the centre of a circle to any point on its circumference

2 Copy and complete the following statement.

The tangent to a circle at a point P is . . . to the radius to that point.

3 Jonah says that the shaded region is not a segment of this circle because it is bigger than half of the circle. Is he correct? Explain your reasoning.

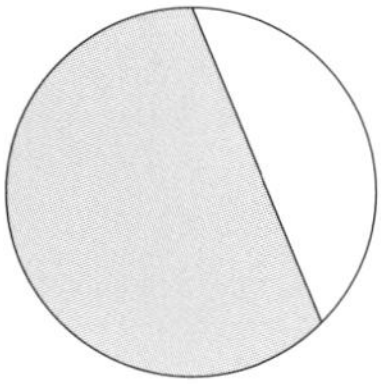

3D–3E Solid shapes

Example

How many:

a vertices

b faces

c edges?

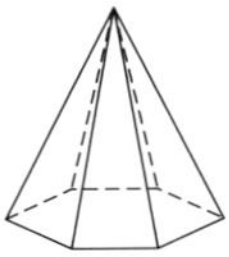

a vertices = 7

b faces = 7

c edges = 12

1 **i**

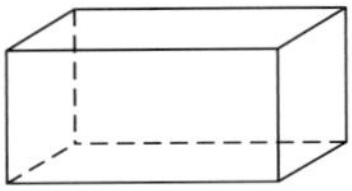

ii

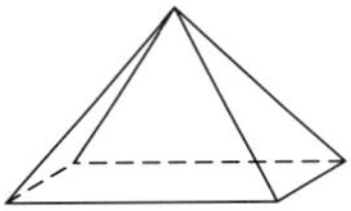

iii

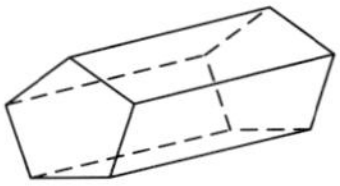

iv

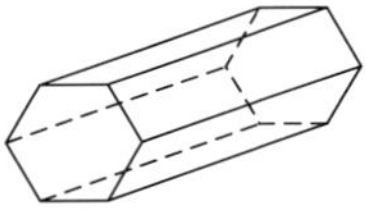

v

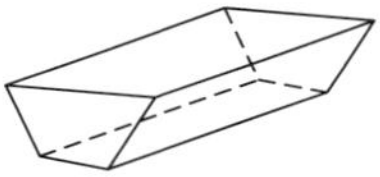

vi

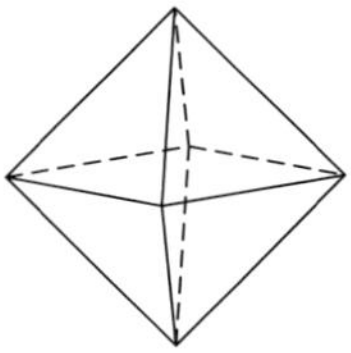

a Copy and complete the table for the shapes shown above.

Shape	Vertices (V)	Faces (F)	Edges (E)
i	8		
ii		5	
iii			15
iv			
v			
vi			

b Write down a rule connecting V, F and E.

c Which of the shapes are cuboids?

d Which of the shapes are prisms?

e Which of the shapes are pyramids?

2 **a** Draw a cylinder.

b Write down another mathematical name to describe your cylinder.

c How many curved surfaces does a cylinder have?

d How many flat surfaces does a cylinder have?

3 A pyramid has 12 edges.

a How many vertices does it have?

b How many faces does it have?

4 A pyramid has 9 faces.

a How many vertices does it have?

b How many edges does it have?

5 A prism has 24 edges.

a How many vertices does it have?

b How many faces does it have?

3F Representing 3D shapes

Example

This object is made from four 1 cm cubes.
Use squared paper to draw the plan, front elevation and side elevation of the object.

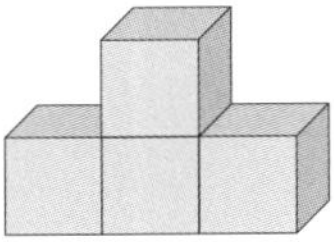

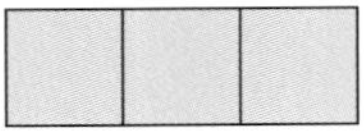
Plan

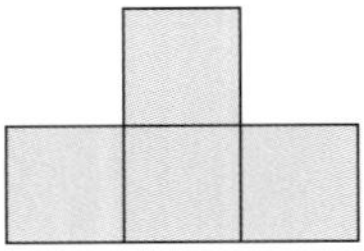
Front

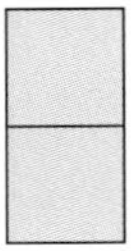
Side

1 Use squared paper to draw the plan, front elevation and side elevation of each of these objects. Each object is made from five 1 cm cubes.

a

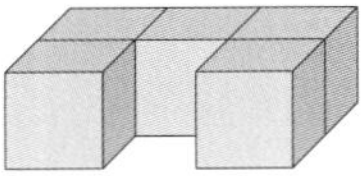

b

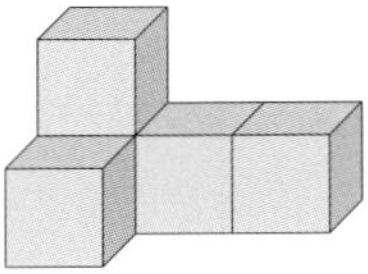

c

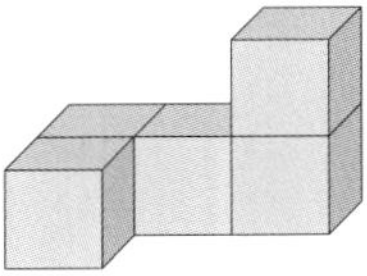

2 Use squared paper to draw the plan, front elevation and side elevation of each of these objects.

a

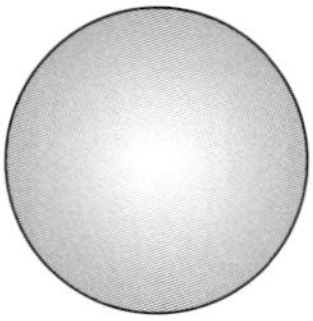
Sphere
radius 3 cm

b

Cylinder
radius 2 cm
height 4 cm

c

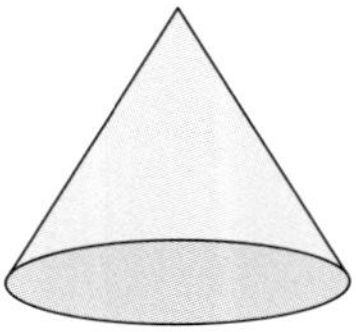
Cone
base radius 3 cm
height 4 cm

3 Use isometric paper to draw the 3D object represented by the plans and elevations.

a

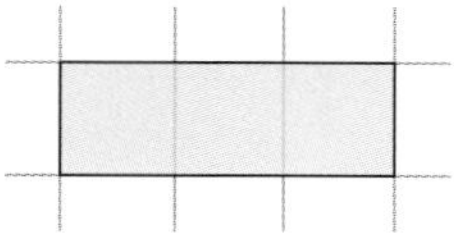

Plan

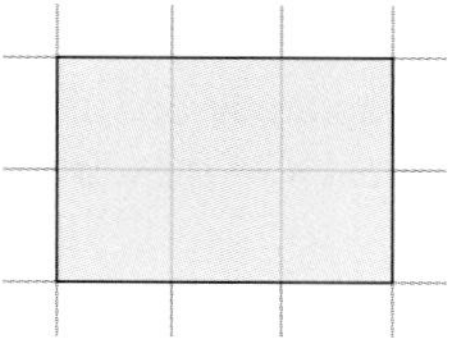

Front

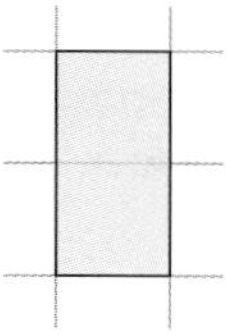

Side

b

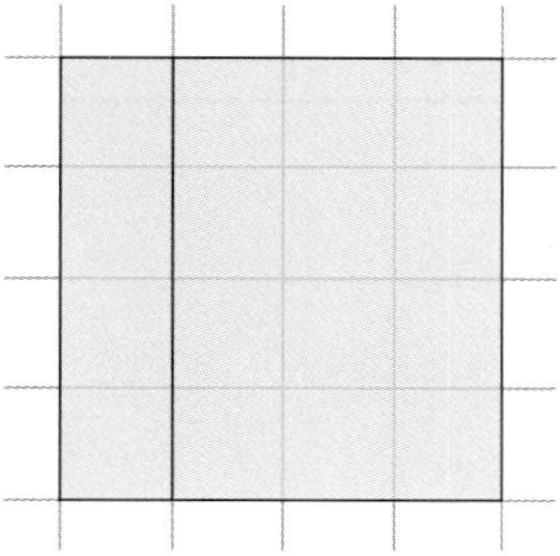

Plan

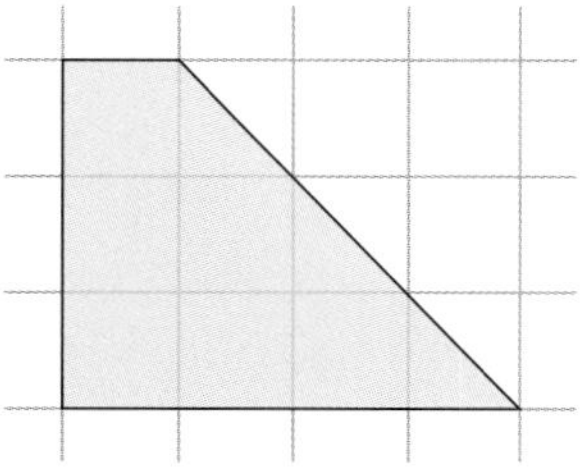

Front

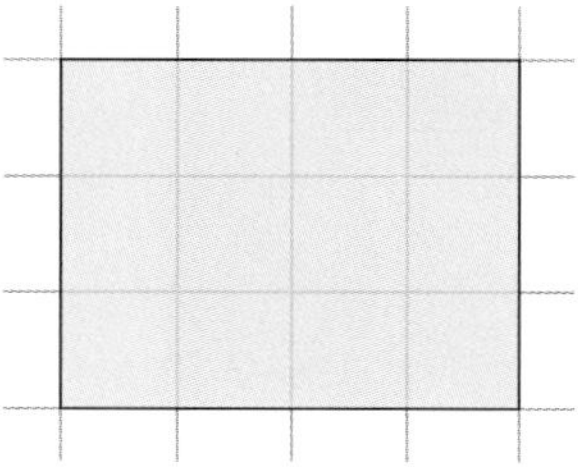

Side

3G Mathematical drawings

Example

a Explain how you can construct an angle of 105° using set squares.
b Explain how you can construct each of these angles using set squares.
i 120° **ii** 135° **iii** 15°

---

a The angles on the two types of set square are 30°, 45°, 60° and 90°.
105° can be made using 60° and 45° because $60° + 45° = 105°$.
b **i** $60° + 60° = 120°$ **ii** $90° + 45° = 135°$ **iii** $60° - 45° = 15°$

1 Using a ruler and a set square, construct:

a a square with side 3.5 cm

b a rectangle measuring 6.2 cm by 7.5 cm

c this parallelogram

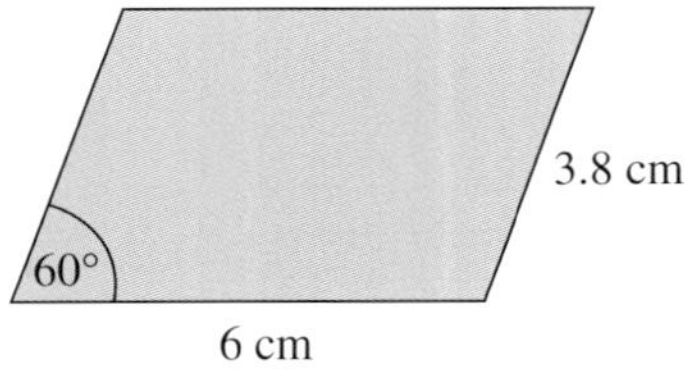

d this rhombus

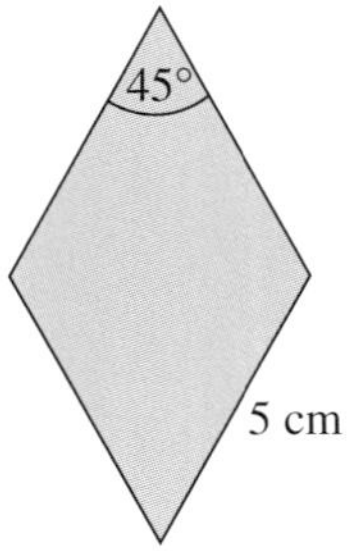

e this isosceles trapezium

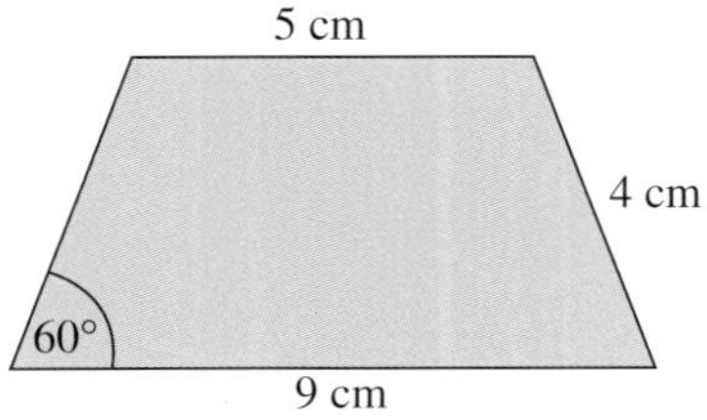

4A Types of data

Example

Decide whether the data is discrete, continuous or neither if it records:

a the number of birds in a field
b the length of a rope
c the time taken to travel to work
d eye colour
e the height of a tree
f the number showing on a dice
g the amount of money in a purse
h the make of a car.

a discrete **b** continuous **c** continuous **d** neither
e continuous **f** discrete **g** discrete **h** neither

1 Is the data numerical or categorical if it records:

a blood type

b the number of employees in a company

c the time taken by an athlete to run 100 m

d the number of eggs in a nest

e hair colour?

2 Is the data discrete or continuous if it records:

a the number of letters in a word

b the length of a leaf

c the profit made by a company

d shoe size

e the mass of an elephant

f a person's height

g the number of pets owned

h the time taken to complete a task?

3 If you collect data in the following ways, is the data primary or secondary?

a You ask athletes at your sports club what their favourite track event is.

b You read on the internet the hottest temperatures recorded in June.

c You ask students at your school what they think of the school canteen service.

d You find the average value of houses in a village using national statistics.

e You find people's favourite colour using the results of a survey taken 5 years ago.

4B–4G Questionnaires and sampling

Example

Khadeeja surveys her classmates to find out how often they go to the cinema. She writes the following question.

How many times do you go to the cinema?

☐	☐	☐
1 – 3	3 – 5	6+

a Explain why this is not a good question.

b Suggest an improved question for Khadeeja to use.

---

a There is no time frame. It should say 'each week' or 'each month' or 'each year'.

There is no response box for people who do not go to the cinema.

There are overlapping boxes. People who go 3 times have two boxes to tick.

b

How many times do you go to the cinema each month?

☐	☐	☐	☐
0	1 – 3	4 – 6	7+

1 Haroon writes the following question.

Experts agree that people watch too much television.
Do you agree that people watch too much television?

Yes ☐ No ☐

Explain why this is not a good question.

2 Omar surveys his classmates to find out how much pocket money they receive.

He writes this question.

How much pocket money do you receive?

☐	☐	☐	☐
$1 – $5	$5 – $10	$10 – $15	$15+

a Explain why this is not a good question.

b Suggest an improved question for Omar to use.

3 A supermarket manager wants to find out about how often people shop at a supermarket. The manager writes the following question.

> How often do you shop at a supermarket?
>
> ☐ Never ☐ Sometimes ☐ Always

a Explain why this is not a good question.

b Suggest an improved question for the manager to use.

4 Danusia designs a questionnaire to find out about her classmates' preferred sports. She only prints 15 copies of her questionnaire. She gives 10 of these copies to her friends and the remaining 5 copies to some of the others in her class.

Explain why this is not a good approach for surveying her class.

5 Priah wants to find out what her year group's favourite subject is. She prints her questionnaire and gives it to the students in her Biology class.

a Explain why this is not a good method of sampling.

b Describe how Priah can improve her data sample.

c Write a suitable question for Priah to use.

6 Anton wants to find out how many holidays people in Spain have each year.

Bethany wants to find out if people in her class prefer burgers or chicken nuggets.

Carlos wants to find out how people in his school travel to school.

Decide whether it would be sensible for each student to take a sample.

a Anton **b** Bethany **c** Carlos

7 Sara wants to find out what students think about their school canteen. She writes the following question.

> In your opinion, what is the best way to improve your school canteen?

Explain why this is not a good question for obtaining data.

8 Design a data collection sheet for the colour of cars in a car park.

9 Design a data collection sheet for boys' and girls' mass and height.

5A Units of area

Example

Convert $6\,m^2$ to square centimetres.

$1\,m^2 = 100 \times 100\,cm^2 = 10\,000\,cm^2$

So, $6\,m^2 = 6 \times 10\,000\,cm^2 = 60\,000\,cm^2$

1 Convert these measurements to square millimetres.

a $5\,cm^2$ **b** $28\,cm^2$ **c** $4.7\,cm^2$ **d** $6.34\,cm^2$

2 Convert these measurements to square centimetres.

a $700\,mm^2$ **b** $90\,mm^2$ **c** $274\,mm^2$ **d** $6273\,mm^2$

3 **a** Find the area of this rectangle in cm^2.

b Write down the area of the rectangle in mm^2.

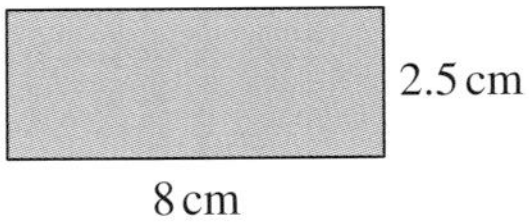

4 Convert these measurements to cm^2.

a $2\,m^2$ **b** $8\,m^2$ **c** $5.8\,m^2$ **d** $0.4\,m^2$

5 Convert these measurements to mm^2.

a $4\,m^2$ **b** $7\,m^2$ **c** $3.9\,m^2$ **d** $0.06\,m^2$

6 Convert these areas to cm^2.

a $3600\,mm^2$ **b** $3.5\,m^2$ **c** $0.8\,km^2$

7 Copy and complete.

a $0.09\,km^2 = \square\,m^2$ **b** $71\,000\,000\,m^2 = \square\,km^2$

c $0.077\,km^2 = \square\,mm^2$ **d** $500\,000\,mm^2 = \square\,m^2$

8 Convert these area measurements to hectares.

a $70\,000\,m^2$ **b** $520\,000\,m^2$ **c** $5000\,m^2$ **d** $300\,m^2$

9 This diagram shows a plot of land.

Find its area, giving your answer in hectares.

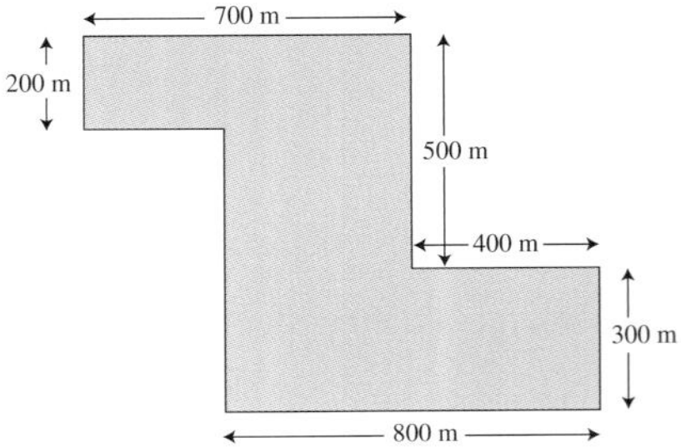

5B–5C Areas of triangles

Example

Calculate the area of the triangle.

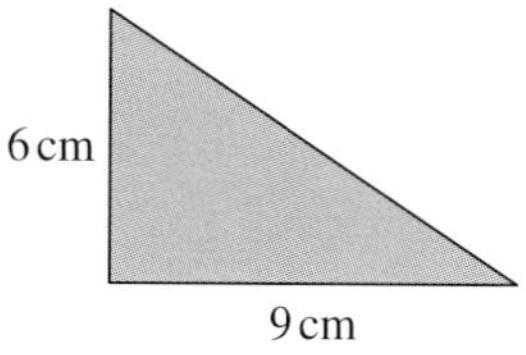

Area of triangle

$= \frac{1}{2} \times \text{base} \times \text{height}$

$= \frac{1}{2} \times 9 \times 6 = 27\,\text{cm}^2$

1 The triangles below have been drawn on a centimetre square grid.

By considering the rectangle surrounding each triangle, find the area of each triangle.

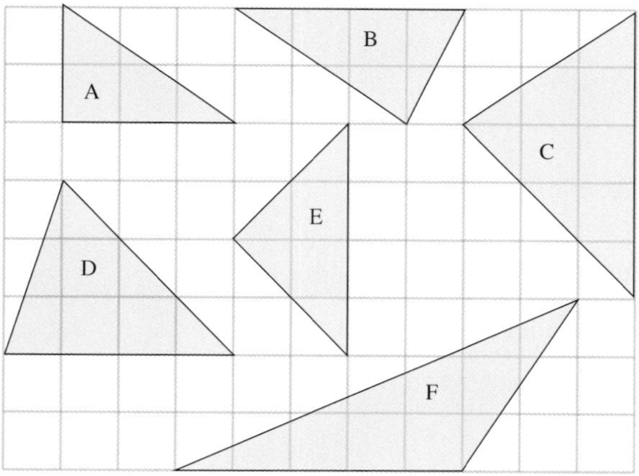

2 Calculate the area of each triangle:

a

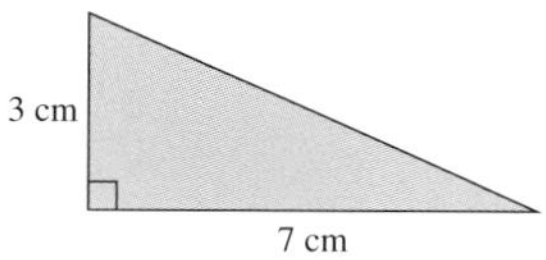

b

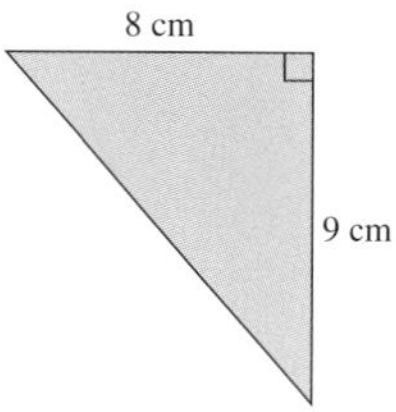

c

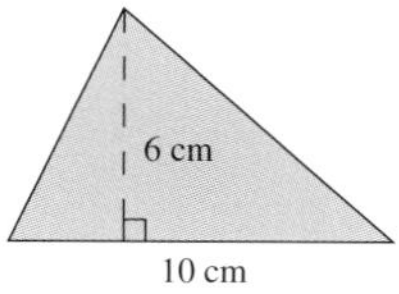

d

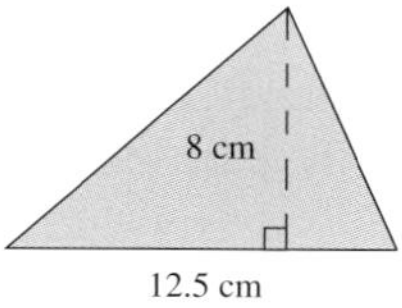

3 The area of this triangle is $29.4\,cm^2$. Find the value of x.

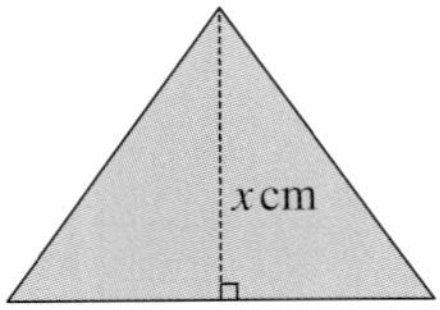

4 The lengths of the two diagonals of a rhombus are 16 cm and 10 cm.

By splitting the rhombus into two congruent triangles, find the area of the rhombus.

5 The lengths of the two diagonals of a kite are 9 cm and 6 cm.

By splitting the kite into two congruent triangles, find the area of the kite.

6 This diagram shows an isosceles trapezium.

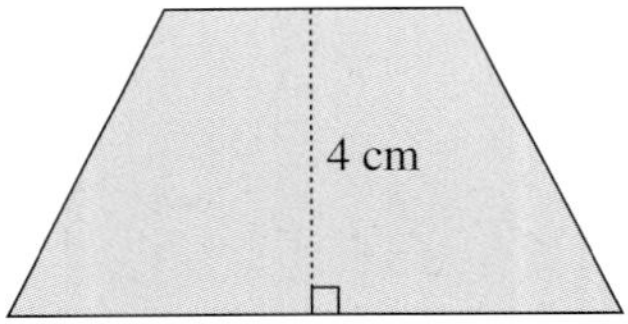

The lengths of the two parallel sides are 6 cm and 3 cm.

The distance between the two parallel sides is 4 cm.

By splitting the trapezium into a rectangle and two triangles, find the area of the trapezium.

7 This diagram shows a parallelogram.

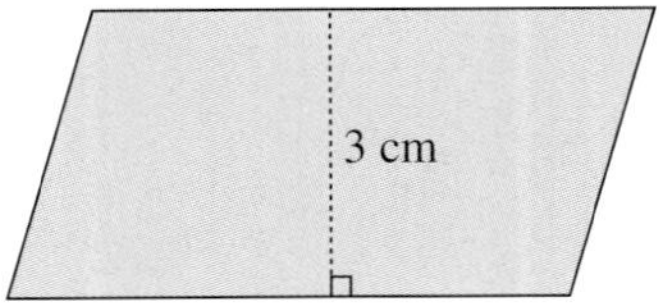

The base of the parallelogram is 5 cm.

The perpendicular height is 3 cm.

By splitting the parallelogram into two congruent triangles, find the area of the parallelogram.

5D–5E Volume

Example

Find the volume of this cuboid.

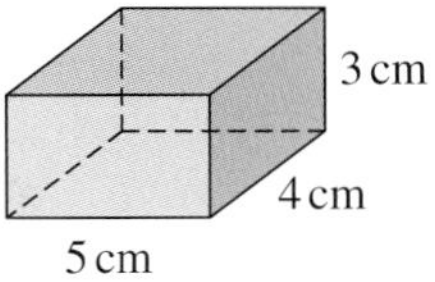

Volume = length × width × height $= 5 \times 4 \times 3 = 60\,\text{cm}^3$

1 These shapes are made of centimetre cubes.
Write down the volume of each shape.

a

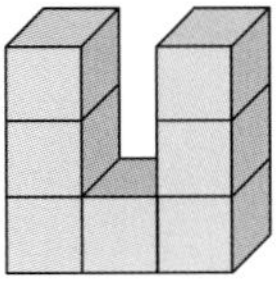

b

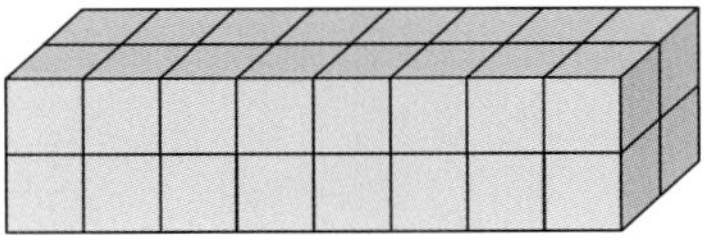

2 Find the volume of these cuboids. The lengths shown are in centimetres.

a

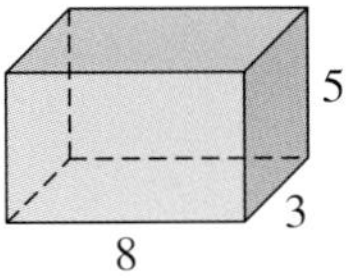

b

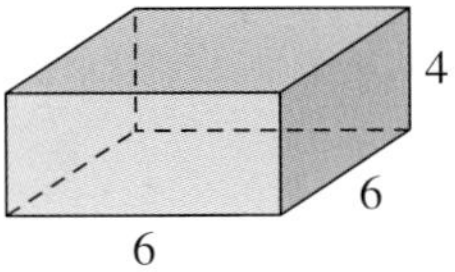

c

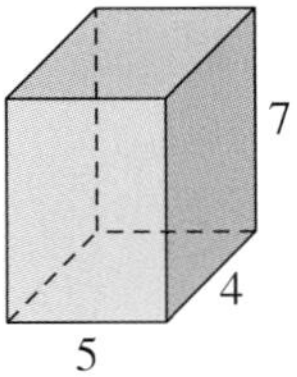

d

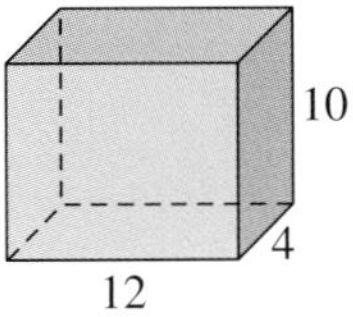

e

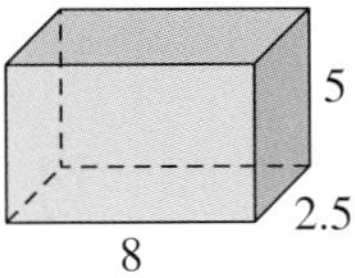

f

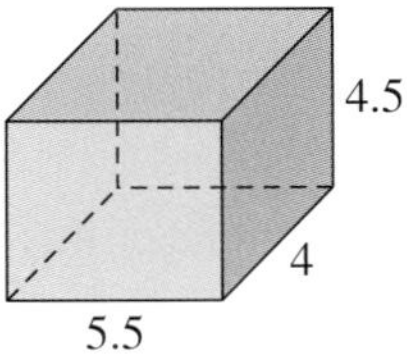

3 A cuboid measures 80 cm by 50 cm by 1 m. Find the volume in:

a cm^3 **b** m^3

4 This cuboid has a volume of $1215\,\text{cm}^3$.
Find the value of x.

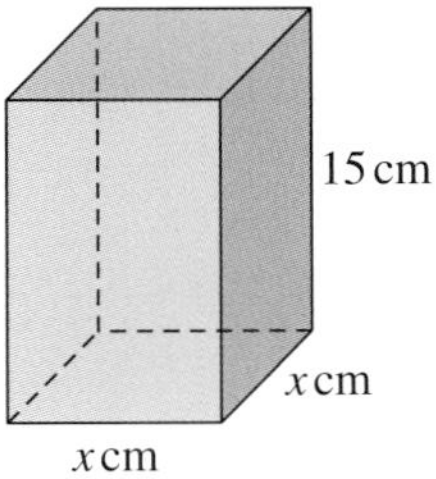

5 **a** Find the volume of this cuboid in m^3.

b Write down the volume of the cuboid in cm^3.

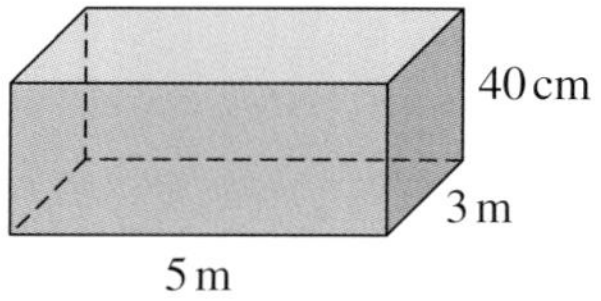

6 Find the volume of this shape. All lengths are in cm.

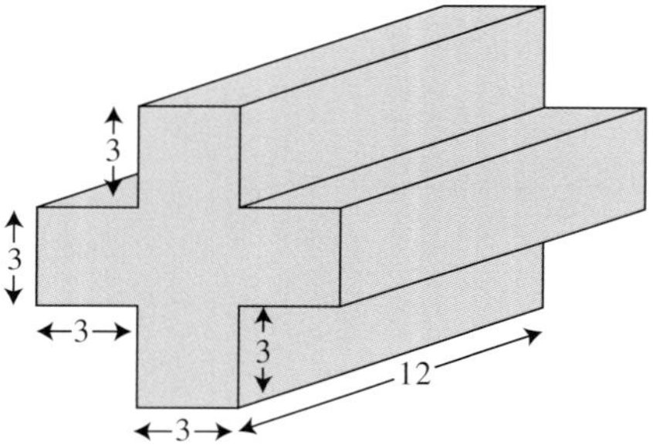

7 Find the missing side lengths in each of these cuboids.

a

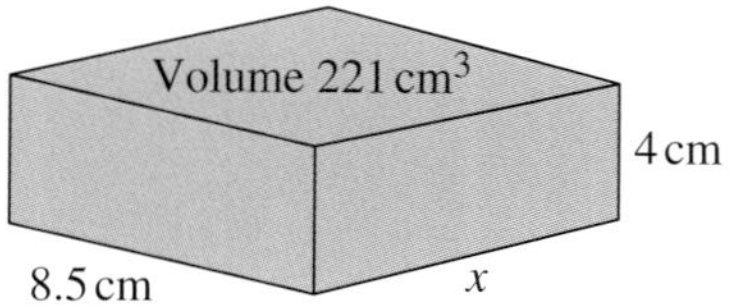

b

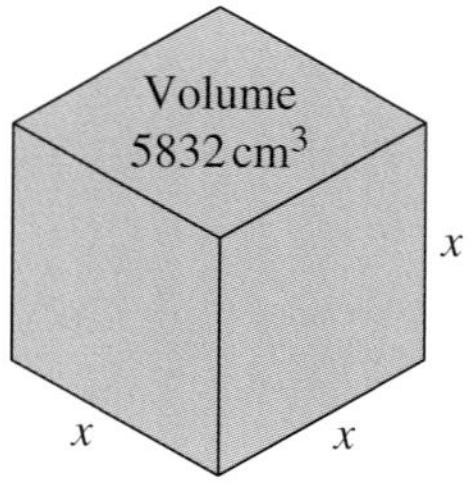

8 Find the volume of this triangular prism.

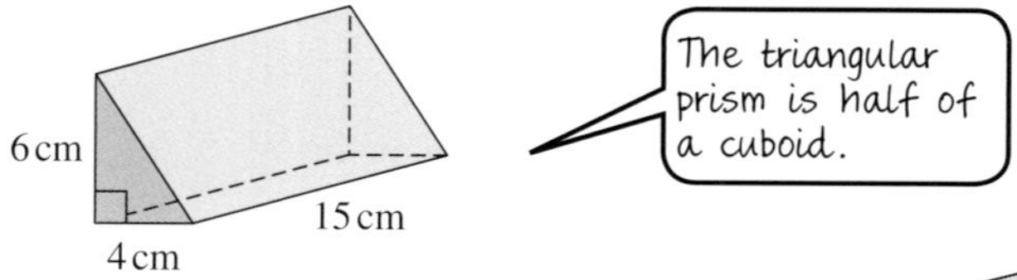

9 The volume of this shape is $1232\,cm^3$.
Find the value of x.

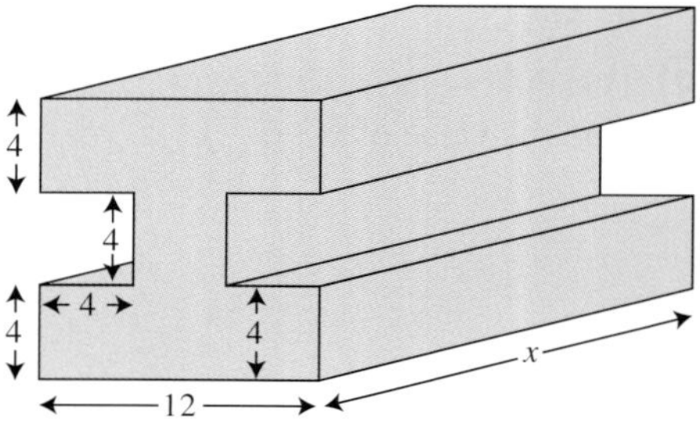

5F Surface area

Example

Find the total surface area of this cuboid.

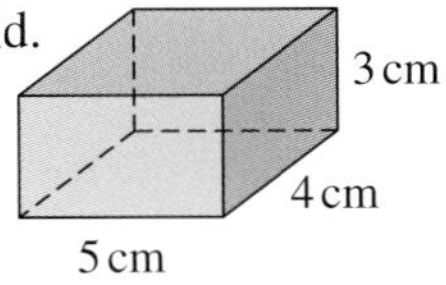

Draw the net:

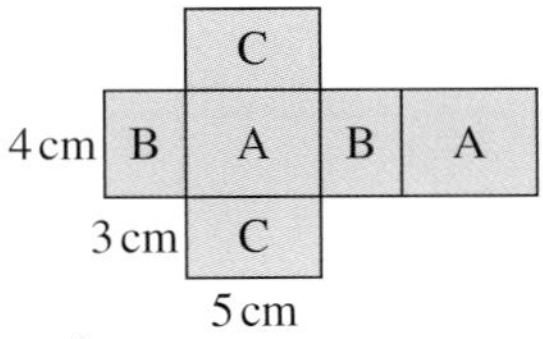

Area A $= 5\,\text{cm} \times 4\,\text{cm} = 20\,\text{cm}^2$

Area B $= 3\,\text{cm} \times 4\,\text{cm} = 12\,\text{cm}^2$

Area C $= 5\,\text{cm} \times 3\,\text{cm} = 15\,\text{cm}^2$

Total surface area $= 2 \times \text{A} + 2 \times \text{B} + 2 \times \text{C}$

$= 40\,\text{cm}^2 + 24\,\text{cm}^2 + 30\,\text{cm}^2$

$= 94\,\text{cm}^2$

1 **a** Find the surface area of a cube with sides of length 4 cm.

b Find the surface area of a cube with sides of length 8 cm.

c Explain what happens to the surface area if you double the lengths.

2 Find the surface area of these cuboids. The lengths shown are in centimetres.

a

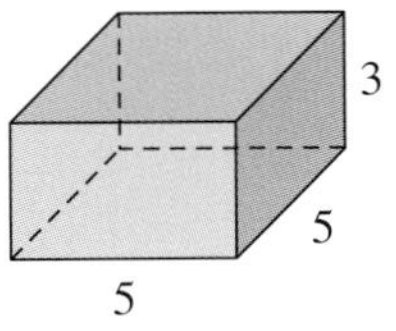

b

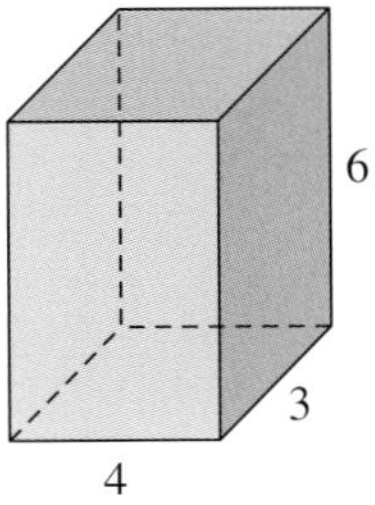

c

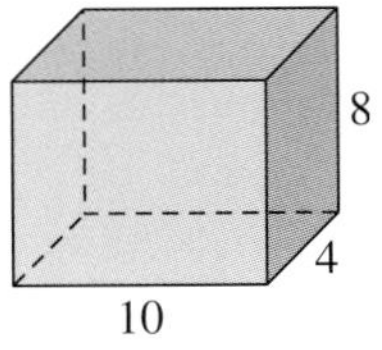

d

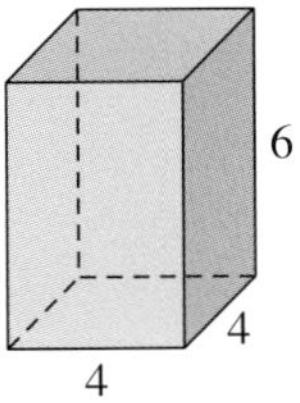

e

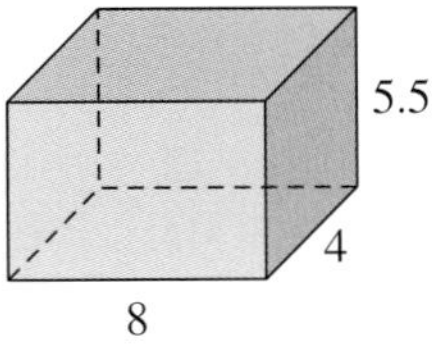

f

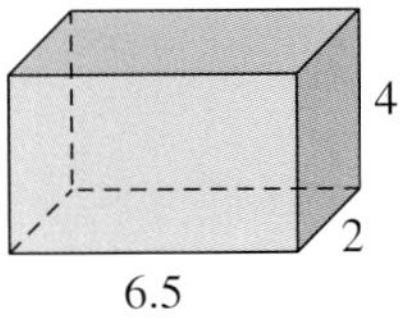

3 A cube has a surface area of $1014\,\text{cm}^2$. Find the length of the sides of the cube.

6A Adding fractions

Example

Calculate: **a** $\frac{2}{5}+\frac{1}{3}$ **b** $2\frac{1}{5}+7\frac{3}{4}$

a $\frac{2}{5}+\frac{1}{3}=\frac{6}{15}+\frac{5}{15}=\frac{11}{15}$

b $2\frac{1}{5}+7\frac{3}{4}=9+\frac{1}{5}+\frac{3}{4}=9+\frac{4}{20}+\frac{15}{20}=9\frac{19}{20}$

1 Calculate:

a $2\frac{1}{3}+1\frac{1}{4}$ **b** $4\frac{2}{3}+2\frac{1}{5}$ **c** $3\frac{1}{6}+2\frac{2}{7}$ **d** $6\frac{2}{5}+4\frac{1}{6}$

e $3\frac{4}{5}+2\frac{5}{6}$ **f** $2\frac{7}{10}+3\frac{4}{9}$ **g** $5\frac{3}{4}+4\frac{3}{5}$ **h** $2\frac{8}{9}+3\frac{2}{3}$

2 Using the diagram below, find the distance between:

a A and C **b** B and D **c** A and D

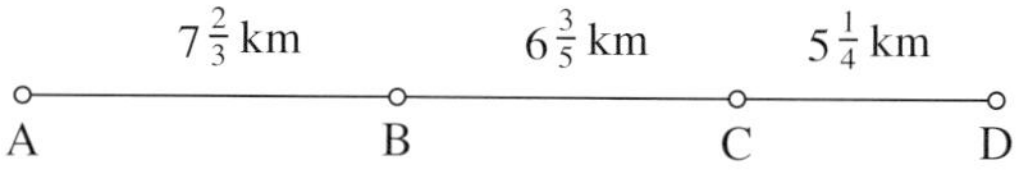

3 Calculate:

a $5\frac{3}{7}+2\frac{2}{3}+4\frac{3}{5}$ **b** $3\frac{5}{8}+2\frac{4}{5}+5\frac{1}{3}$ **c** $2\frac{5}{6}+3\frac{4}{5}+4\frac{3}{4}$

4 In this diagram, the numbers in two circles add to give the number in the square between them.

Find the missing numbers.

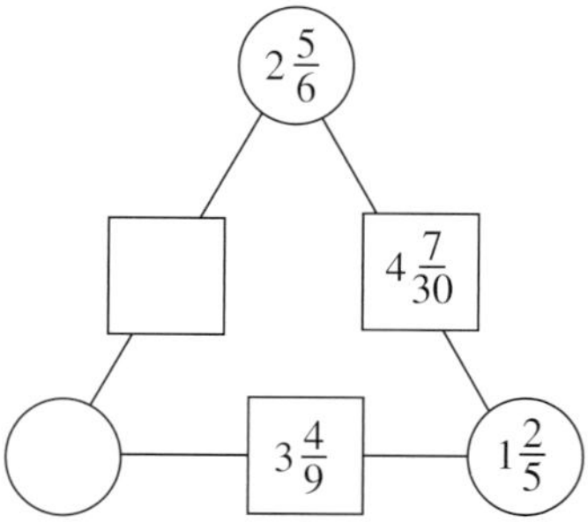

5 Find the missing numbers.

a $3\frac{\square}{4}+1\frac{2}{3}=5\frac{5}{12}$ **b** $3\frac{9}{10}+\frac{\square}{15}=4\frac{11}{30}$

6B Multiplying fractions

Example

Calculate: **a** $5 \times \frac{3}{8}$ **b** $\frac{1}{4} \times \frac{3}{5}$

a $5 \times \frac{3}{8} = \frac{5}{1} \times \frac{3}{8} = \frac{5 \times 3}{1 \times 8} = \frac{15}{8} = 1\frac{7}{8}$

b $\frac{1}{4} \times \frac{3}{5} = \frac{1 \times 3}{4 \times 5} = \frac{3}{20}$

1 Calculate:

a $3 \times \frac{1}{2}$ **b** $\frac{6}{7} \times 2$ **c** $5 \times \frac{8}{9}$

d $4 \times \frac{2}{5}$ **e** $\frac{9}{11} \times 7$ **f** $8 \times \frac{2}{3}$

g $7 \times \frac{5}{14}$ **h** $15 \times \frac{4}{5}$ **i** $\frac{3}{16} \times 24$

2 Calculate:

a $\frac{4}{5} \times \frac{1}{2}$ **b** $\frac{3}{4} \times \frac{6}{11}$ **c** $\frac{2}{3} \times \frac{3}{5}$

d $\frac{4}{7} \times \frac{5}{6}$ **e** $\frac{3}{5} \times \frac{10}{11}$ **f** $\frac{6}{13} \times \frac{5}{12}$

g $\frac{4}{9} \times \frac{5}{12}$ **h** $\frac{8}{11} \times \frac{5}{6}$ **i** $\frac{7}{15} \times \frac{3}{5}$

3 Work out the following. Remember to cancel before multiplying the fractions.

a $\frac{14}{15} \times \frac{12}{49}$ **b** $\frac{11}{16} \times \frac{24}{33}$ **c** $\frac{13}{20} \times \frac{35}{39}$

d $\frac{17}{25} \times \frac{15}{34}$ **e** $\frac{23}{70} \times \frac{21}{46}$ **f** $\frac{16}{17} \times \frac{51}{64}$

4 Calculate:

a $\frac{2}{5} \times \frac{1}{2} \times \frac{5}{9}$ **b** $\frac{3}{4} \times \frac{6}{7} \times \frac{8}{15}$ **c** $\frac{2}{3} \times \frac{8}{9} \times \frac{6}{7}$

d $\frac{6}{7} \times \frac{2}{5} \times \frac{14}{15}$ **e** $\frac{4}{5} \times \frac{9}{10} \times \frac{15}{16}$ **f** $\frac{6}{11} \times \frac{8}{9} \times \frac{3}{4}$

5 Find the area of this rectangle.

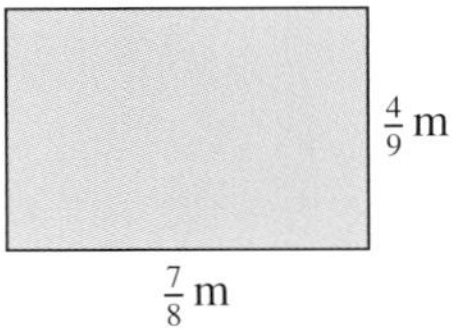

6 x and y are positive integers and $\frac{x}{y} \times \frac{4}{9} = \frac{y}{x}$. Find the value of x and the value of y.

6C Dividing fractions

Example

Calculate: **a** $\frac{1}{4} \surd \frac{2}{5}$ **b** $\frac{2}{3} \surd \frac{5}{9}$

a $\frac{1}{4} \div \frac{2}{5} = \frac{1}{4} \times \frac{5}{2} = \frac{1 \times 5}{4 \times 2} = \frac{5}{8}$

b $\frac{2}{3} \div \frac{5}{9} = \frac{2}{\cancel{3}_1} \times \frac{\cancel{9}^3}{5} = \frac{2 \times 3}{1 \times 5} = \frac{6}{5} = 1\frac{1}{5}$

1 Write down the reciprocal of these numbers.

a $\frac{5}{6}$ **b** $\frac{7}{10}$ **c** $\frac{3}{5}$

d 5 **e** $\frac{5}{4}$ **f** $1\frac{4}{9}$

2 Calculate:

a $\frac{2}{5} \surd \frac{1}{2}$ **b** $\frac{3}{4} \surd \frac{6}{7}$ **c** $\frac{2}{3} \surd \frac{8}{9}$

d $\frac{6}{7} \surd \frac{2}{5}$ **e** $\frac{4}{5} \surd \frac{9}{10}$ **f** $\frac{6}{11} \surd \frac{8}{9}$

g $\frac{5}{6} \surd \frac{2}{7}$ **h** $\frac{8}{9} \surd \frac{2}{5}$ **i** $\frac{7}{12} \surd \frac{1}{4}$

3 Find the missing numbers.

a $\frac{5}{9} \times \frac{\square}{\square} = \frac{1}{3}$ **b** $\frac{\square}{\square} \times \frac{8}{9} = \frac{7}{27}$

4 A rectangle has area $\frac{3}{4}\,\text{m}^2$ and width $\frac{1}{3}\,\text{m}$.

Find the length of the rectangle.

5 Find the missing numbers.

a $\frac{1}{6} \div \frac{\square}{\square} = \frac{1}{4}$ **b** $\frac{7}{10} \div \frac{\square}{\square} = \frac{14}{15}$ **c** $\frac{4}{5} \div \frac{\square}{\square} = 1\frac{1}{5}$

6 In this diagram, the numbers in two circles multiply to give the number in the square between them.

Find the missing numbers.

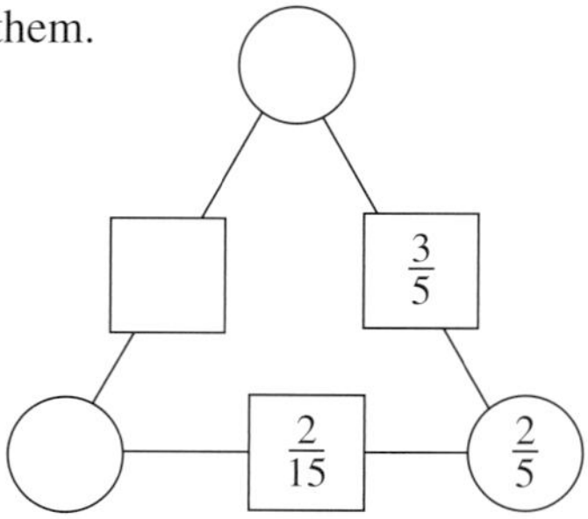

6D Simplifying calculations with fractions

Example

Calculate: **a** $\frac{4}{7}+6\frac{5}{8}+\frac{3}{7}$ **b** $5\times 23\frac{2}{9}$

a $\frac{4}{7}+6\frac{5}{8}+\frac{3}{7}=\frac{4}{7}+\frac{3}{7}+6\frac{5}{8}=\frac{7}{7}+6\frac{5}{8}=1+6\frac{5}{8}=7\frac{5}{8}$

b $5\times 23\frac{2}{9}=5\times\left(23+\frac{2}{9}\right)=5\times 23+5\times\frac{2}{9}=115+\frac{10}{9}=115+1\frac{1}{9}=116\frac{1}{9}$

1 Work out, using a quick method:

a $\frac{2}{3}+1\frac{3}{4}+\frac{1}{3}$ **b** $\frac{5}{8}+4\frac{3}{11}+\frac{3}{8}$ **c** $\frac{7}{9}+5\frac{4}{11}+\frac{2}{9}$

d $\frac{3}{4}\times\frac{2}{5}\times 12$ **e** $18\times\frac{4}{5}\times\frac{2}{3}$ **f** $\frac{5}{14}\times\frac{5}{6}\times 28$

g $3\times 14\frac{1}{6}$ **h** $4\times 31\frac{3}{4}$ **i** $8\times 30\frac{2}{3}$

2 Work out:

a $\frac{3}{4}+2\times\frac{5}{8}$ **b** $\left(\frac{3}{4}+\frac{1}{3}\right)\times\left(5+\frac{1}{5}\right)$ **c** $2\frac{1}{2}+3\div\frac{2}{3}+\frac{1}{5}$

d $4\times 3\frac{1}{4}+5\div 1\frac{2}{3}$ **e** $8\div\left(1\frac{2}{3}+1\frac{1}{5}\right)$ **f** $3\times\left(\frac{3}{4}+\frac{1}{5}\right)+9$

g $3\times 2\frac{1}{4}+1\frac{1}{10}$ **h** $11\div 2\frac{1}{5}+2\times\frac{3}{8}$ **i** $\frac{1}{2}+\frac{2}{3}\times 9+5\div 1\frac{1}{4}$

3 The masses of three newborn babies are $3\frac{7}{10}$ kg, $3\frac{2}{3}$ kg and $4\frac{3}{10}$ kg.

Find the total mass of the babies.

4 The cuboid has side lengths $\frac{4}{9}$ cm, $\frac{3}{8}$ cm and 12 cm.

Find the volume of the cuboid.

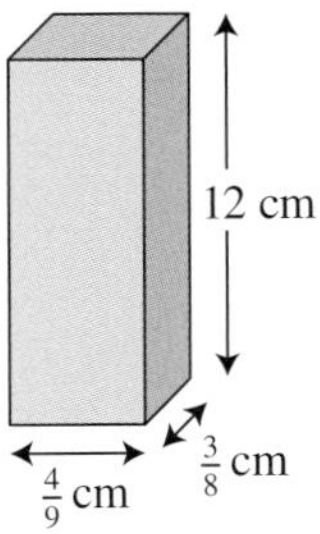

7A Substituting into expressions

Example

When $x = 5$ and $y = 7$, find the value of:

a $2xy$ **b** $8x - 2y$ **c** $3y(11 - x)$

---

a $2xy = 2 \times 5 \times 7$

$= 70$

b $8x - 2y = 8 \times 5 - 2 \times 7$

$= 40 - 14$

$= 26$

c $3y(11 - x) = 3 \times 7 \times (11 - 5)$

$= 3 \times 7 \times 6$

$= 126$

1 When $x = 6$, find the value of:

a $5x$ **b** $2x - 3$ **c** $8x + 5$ **d** $12 - 2x$

e $4(x + 3)$ **f** x^2 **g** $3x^2 + 1$ **h** $x(3 + x)$

2 When $a = 4$ and $b = 9$, find the value of:

a $4a + b$ **b** $7a - 2b$ **c** $3b - a$ **d** $23 + 4b$

e $3(a + b)$ **f** $a^2 - b$ **g** $3b^2 - 2$ **h** $2b(14 - 3a)$

i $\frac{b - a}{5}$ **j** $\frac{2a + 10}{b}$ **k** $\frac{b^2 + a}{5}$ **l** $\frac{3 + b}{a}$

3 When $p = 2$, $q = 4$ and $r = 3$, find the value of:

a pqr **b** $5qr + p$ **c** $pq + r$ **d** $p^2 + q^2 + r^2$

e $5p - 2q$ **f** $pr - 9$ **g** $2(3p + 2q)$ **h** $7p + q - r$

i $\frac{p + q}{r}$ **j** $\frac{q - p}{p}$ **k** $\frac{5q + 4r}{p}$ **l** $\frac{pr}{q}$

4

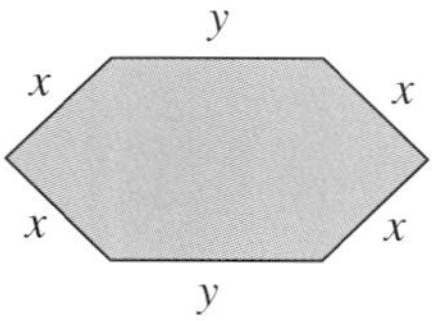

a Write down an expression for the perimeter of this shape.

b Find the perimeter when $x = 3$ cm and $y = 5$ cm.

c Find the perimeter when $x = 2\frac{4}{5}$ cm and $y = 4\frac{1}{3}$ cm.

7B Writing formulae

Example

The cost of hiring a car is made up of two parts.
Write down a formula for the total cost, T dollars, of hiring a car for n days.
Use your formula to find the total cost of hiring a car for 5 days.

Fixed fee: $60
AND THEN
$25 per day

Formula: $T = 60 + 25n$

Total cost: $T = 60 + 25 \times 5 = 60 + 125 = \$185$

1 Cinema tickets cost $8 each.

Write down a formula for the total cost, C, of buying t cinema tickets.

2 A bus can carry n passengers.

Write down a formula for the total number of passengers, P, that can be carried by b buses.

3 A tank contains x litres of oil.

y litres of oil are removed from the tank.

Write down a formula for the number of litres of oil, N, remaining in the tank.

4 Write down a formula for the total cost, C, of buying x ice lollies and y ice creams.

	Ice lollies	$2 each
	Ice creams	$3 each

5 Write down a formula for the total cost, C, of x adult tickets and y child tickets.

★ ENTRY TICKETS ★

Adult ticket	$5 each
Child ticket	$3 each

7C–7D Using and rearranging formulae

Example

The current exchange rate between euros and US dollars is: €1 = $1.26

a Write down a formula to convert E euros (€) into D dollars ($).

b Use your formula to convert €500 into dollars.

---

a Number of dollars = 1.26 × number of euros

$$D = 1.26E$$

b $D = 1.26 \times 500 = 630$

Answer: $630

1 **a** Write down a formula to convert m metres into c centimetres.

b Use the formula from part **a** to convert 5.8 metres into centimetres.

2 The current exchange rate between pounds and US dollars is: £1 = $1.38

a Write down a formula to convert P pounds (£) into D dollars ($).

b Use the formula from part **a** to convert £300 into dollars.

3 The cost of hiring a tent is made up of two parts.

Fixed fee: $20
AND THEN
$5 per day

a Write down a formula for the total cost, T dollars, of hiring a tent for n days.

b Use the formula from part **a** to find the total cost of hiring a tent for 12 days.

4 Rearrange these formulae to make x the subject.

a $3x = y$ **b** $7x = m$ **c** $x + 2 = y$ **d** $x - 4 = y$

e $5 + x = p$ **f** $\frac{x}{a} = b$ **g** $\frac{x}{y} = c$ **h** $xy = 4$

5 Write down as many formulae as you can that can be rearranged to give $2p - q = r$.

7E–7F Solving equations

Example

Solve: **a** $2x + 7 = 15$ **b** $3y - 8 = 13$

a $2x + 7 = 15$
$2x = 8$
$x = 4$

b $3y - 8 = 13$
$3y = 21$
$y = 7$

1 Write these balance drawings as equations.

a

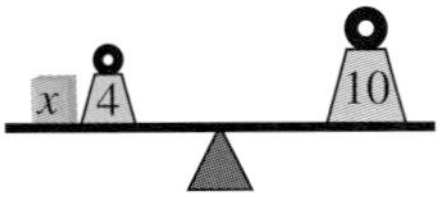

b

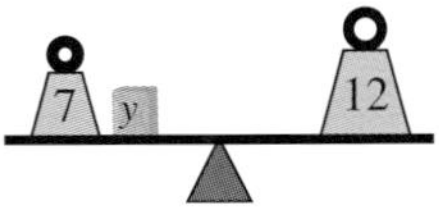

c

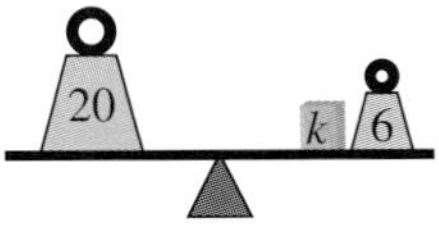

d Solve each equation to calculate the mass of each box marked with a letter. Use balancing operations.

2 Solve these equations.

a $x + 3 = 7$ **b** $x + 4 = 9$ **c** $8 + x = 10$ **d** $9 = x + 2$

e $x - 4 = 6$ **f** $x - 7 = 9$ **g** $x + 5 = 7$ **h** $x - 4 = {}^{-}6$

i $x - 9 = {}^{-}3$ **j** $5x = 30$ **k** $7x = 63$ **l** $4x = 32$

m $40 = 8x$ **n** $0 = 2x$ **o** $54 = 3x$ **p** $2x = 9$

q $3x = 1$ **r** $4x = 17$

3 Solve these equations.

a $2x + 3 = 9$ **b** $3x + 5 = 26$ **c** $4x + 2 = 34$ **d** $5x + 1 = 31$

e $6x + 5 = 47$ **f** $4x + 6 = 42$ **g** $3x - 2 = 10$ **h** $2x - 7 = 13$

i $4x - 8 = 36$ **j** $12 - 7x = 2$ **k** $20 - 3x = 26$ **l** $4 - 3x = 19$

m $2x + 1 = 6$ **n** $3x - 5 = 2$ **o** $4x + 3 = 10$

4 Solve the equations. Match each answer with a number card.

9 $^{-}2$ 4 7 $3\frac{1}{2}$ 6

a $12 + 3x = 24$ **b** $20 = 27 - 2x$ **c** $15 - 2x = 19$

d $4x + 3 - x = 30$ **e** $50 = 6x + 2 + 2x$ **f** $23 + 2x + 6 - 5x = 8$

7G Using equations to solve problems

Example

The length of a rectangle is three times its width.
The perimeter of the rectangle is 72 cm.
Find the width of the rectangle.

Perimeter $= 72$

$3x + x + 3x + x = 72$

$8x = 72$

$x = 9$

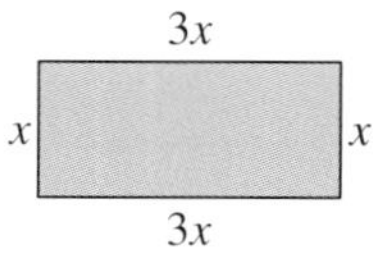

Width = 9 cm

1 For each of these statements, form an equation in x then solve it to find x.

a If we multiply x by 4 the answer is 52.

b If we multiply x by 3 and then add 6 the answer is 27.

c If we multiply x by 2 and then take away 8 the answer is 10.

d If we multiply x by 7 and then add $\frac{1}{2}$ the answer is 18.

2 The length of a rectangle is twice its width.
The perimeter is 54 cm.

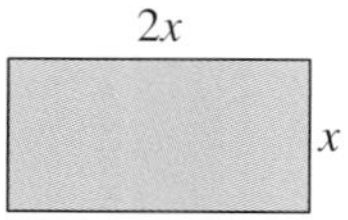

a Write down an equation in x.

b Solve your equation to find the value of x.

3 This rectangle has a perimeter of 60 cm.

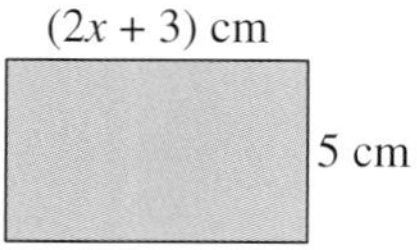

a Write down an equation in x.

b Solve your equation to find the value of x.

4 These number walls are made by adding two adjacent numbers to obtain the number above. Find the value of x for each of the walls.

a

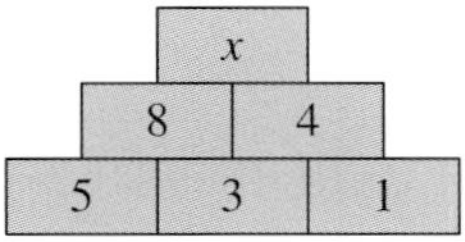

b

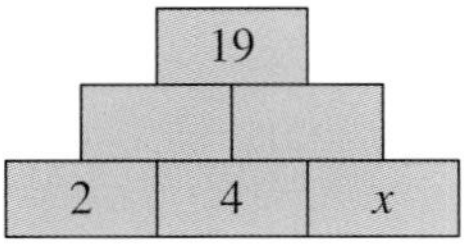

c

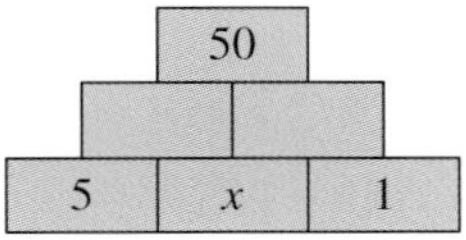

5 \$150 is shared between Diyana and Colin.
Diyana receives \$27 more than Colin.
How much does Diyana receive?

7H Inequalities

Example

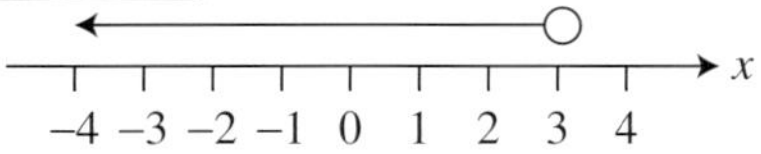

a Write down the inequality shown by this number line.
b Write down the largest integer x could be.

---

a All the values on the arrow are smaller than 3 so $x < 3$.
b The largest integer x could be is 2.

1 Copy and complete the following, using < or > in place of the boxes.

a 5 □ 8   **b** 7 □ 2   **c** $^-1$ □ 3

d 15 □ 6   **e** $^-7$ □ $^-9$ **f** $^-2$ □ 6

2 Represent these inequalities on a number line.

a $x > 2$ **b** $x < 4$

3 Write down the inequalities shown on these number lines.

a

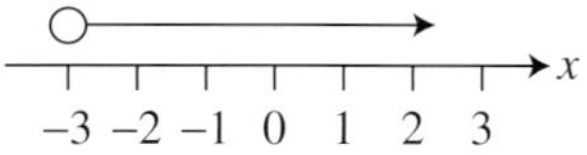

b

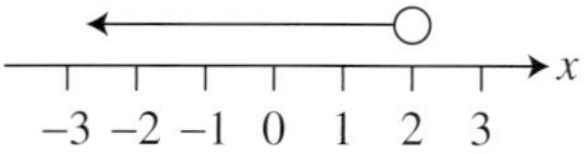

c

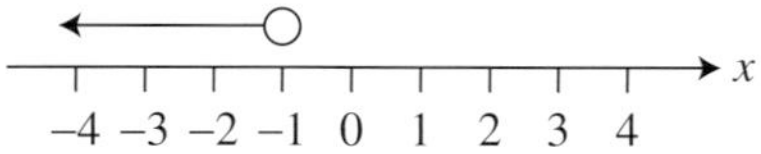

4 **a** What is the smallest integer that x could be in question **3a**?

b What is the largest integer that x could be in question **3b**?

c What is the largest integer that x could be in question **3c**?

5 What is the smallest negative integer that satisfies the inequality $x > {}^-4$?

6 Jonas has x apples. Write an inequality to represent each of these statements.

a Jonas has more than 5 apples.

b Jonas has less than 9 apples.

7 In the Venn diagram, x is a single-digit positive integer.

Copy and complete the Venn diagram, showing all possible values of x.

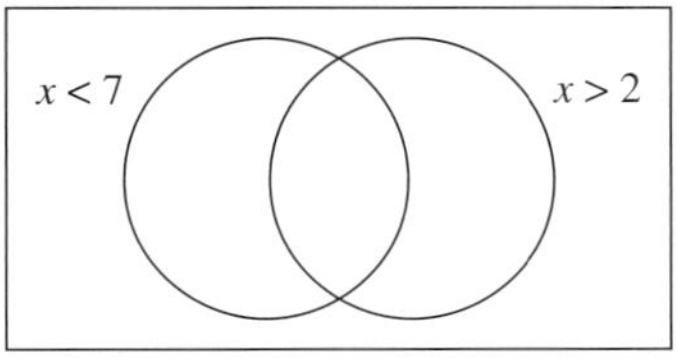

8A Angles around a point

Example

Find the size of the angle marked x.

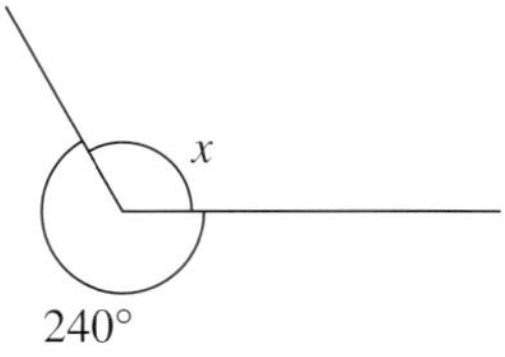

Angles at a point add up to 360°

$x + 240° = 360°$

$x = 120°$

In questions **1** to **11**, find the size of the unknown angles, without measuring.

1

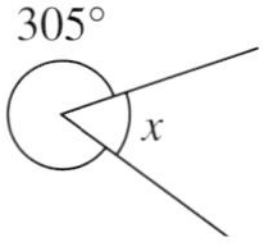

2

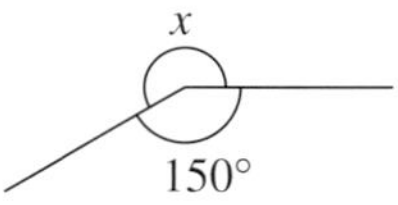

3

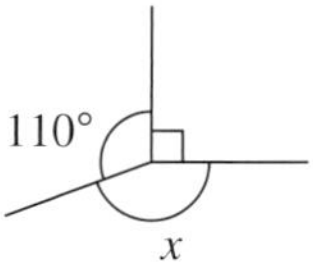

4

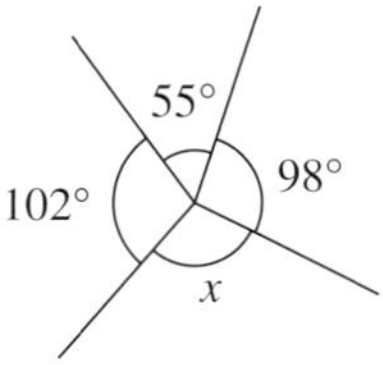

5

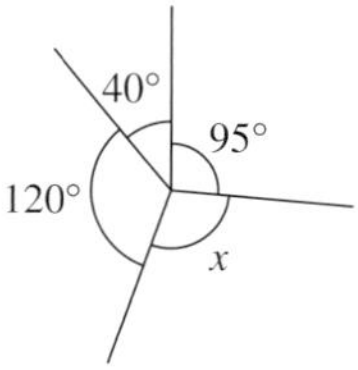

6

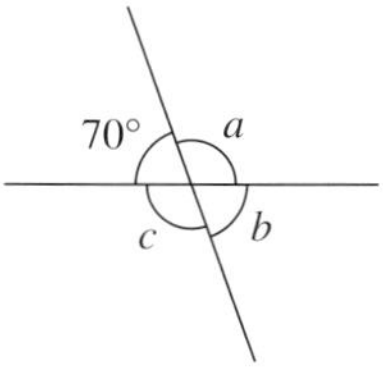

7

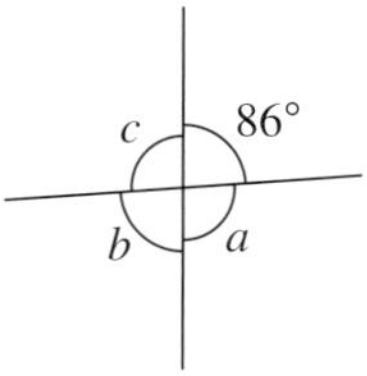

8

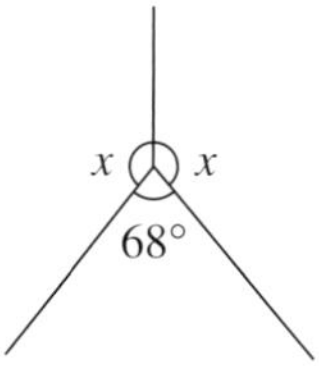

9

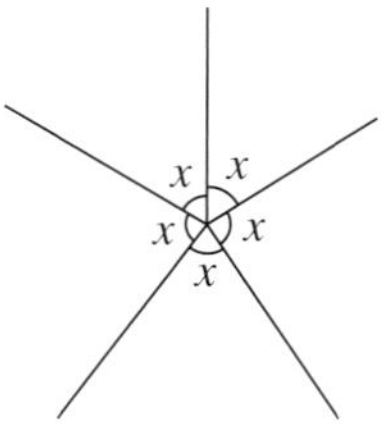

10

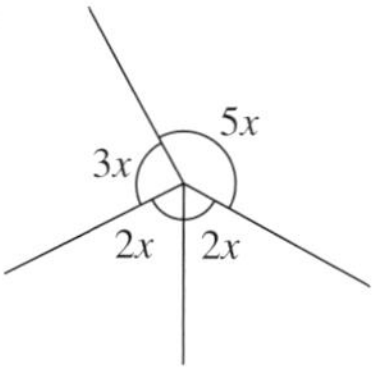

11

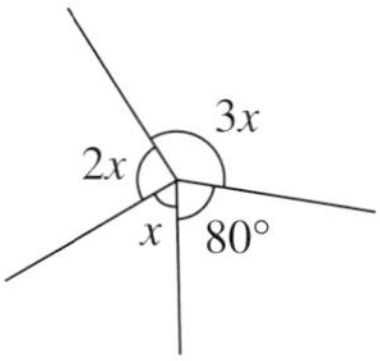

12 Aiman draws four angles of 93°, 59°, 112° and 95°.

He says "I can fit these angles around a point and there will be no gap."

Is Aiman correct? Explain your answer.

8B Angles in quadrilaterals

Example

Find the size of the angle marked x.

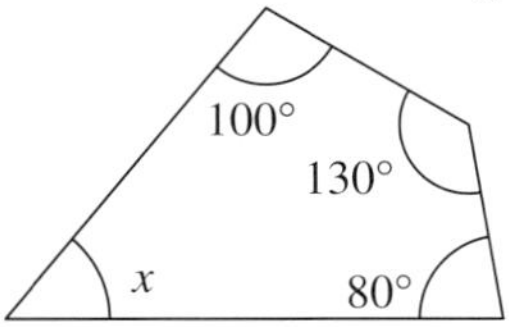

Angles in a quadrilateral add up to 360°.

$x + 100 + 130 + 80 = 360°$

$x + 310 = 360°$

$x = 50°$

In questions **1** to **3**, find the size of the unknown angles, without measuring.

1

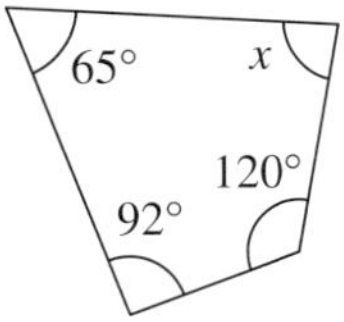

2

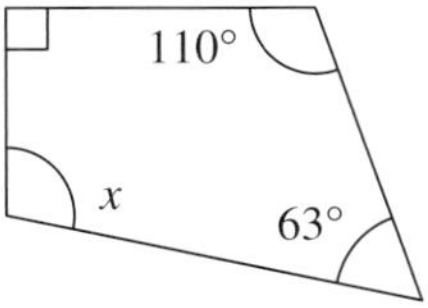

3

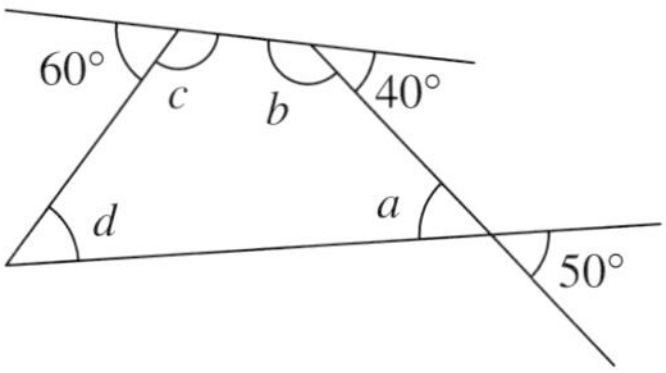

4 Suki says that it is not possible to draw a quadrilateral with the angles shown here. Is Suki correct? Explain your answer.

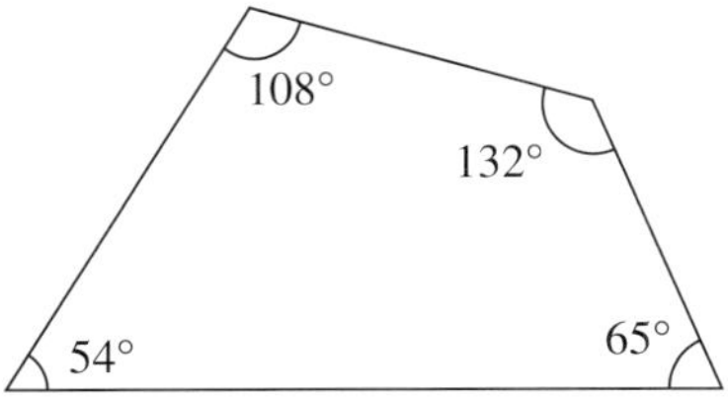

5 **a** Copy and complete this statement. In quadrilateral ABCD, $a + c = \ldots$

b Write down a pair of possible values for a and c.

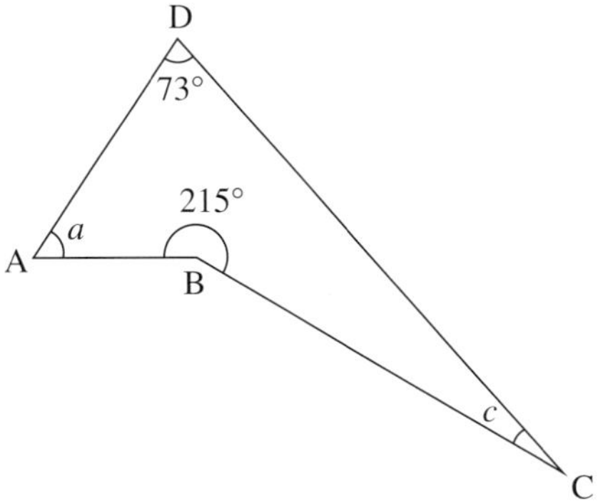

8C–8D Angles in parallel lines

Example

Find the size of the unknown angles.

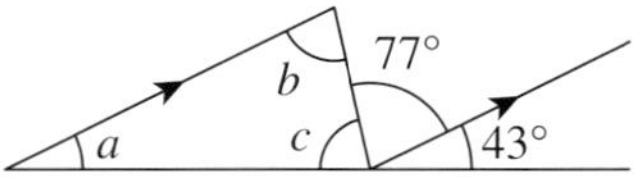

$a = 43°$ (corresponding angles)
$b = 77°$ (alternate angles)
$c = 180° - 77° - 43° = 60°$
(angles in a triangle or on a straight line)

Find the size of the unknown angles.

1

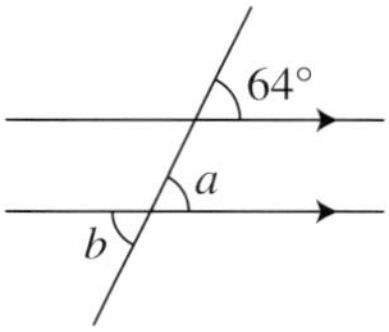

2

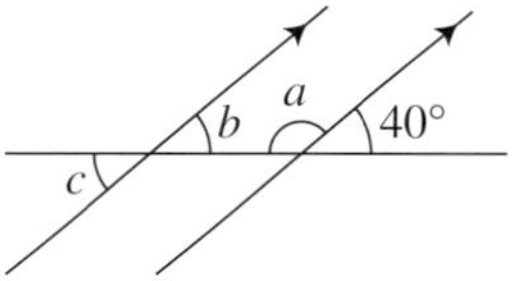

3

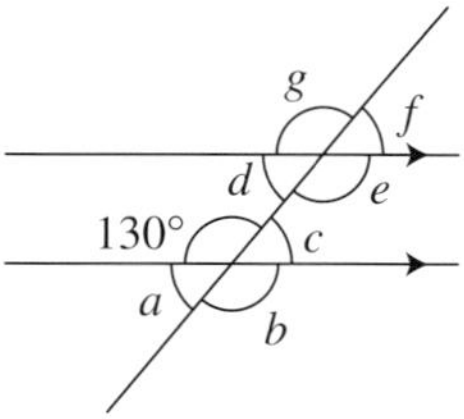

4

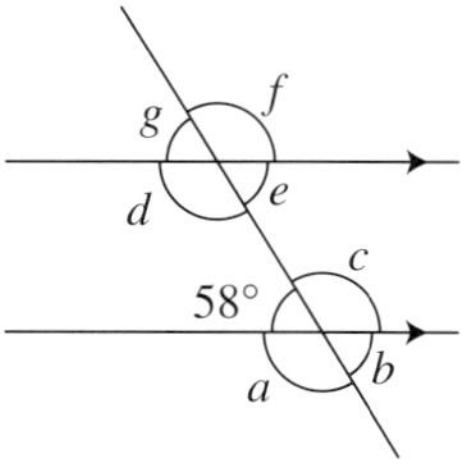

5

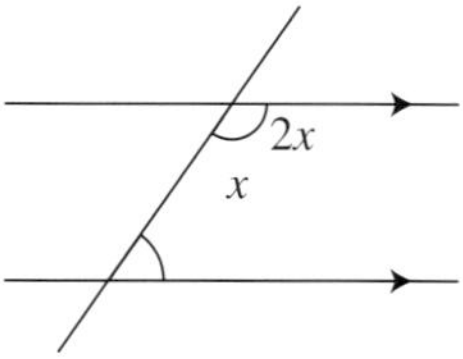

6

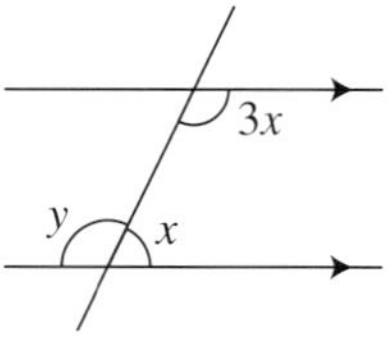

7

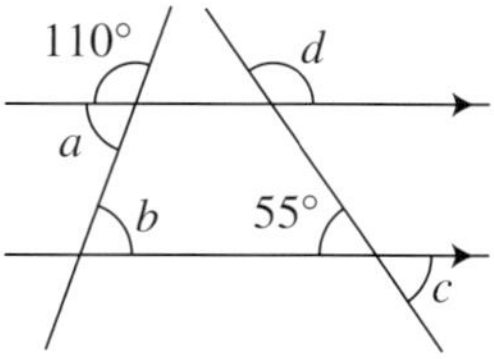

8

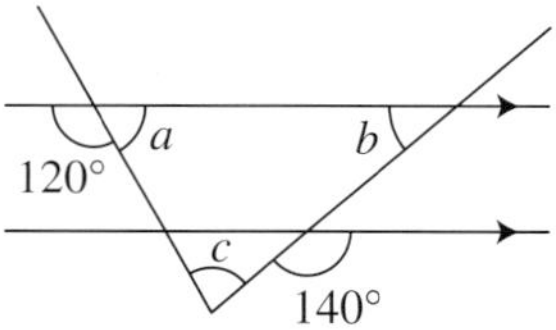

8E Distance between coordinates

Example

Find the distance between the points A = ($^{-}2$, $^{-}4$) and B = (9, $^{-}4$).

The y-coordinates are the same for both A and B, which means A and B lie on the same horizontal line, $y = {}^{-}4$.

Point B is 9 units to the right of the y-axis and point A is 2 units to the left of the y-axis.

Distance between A and B = 9 + 2 = 11

Try to do all of these questions without drawing on squared paper.

1 Which of these points lie on the same **vertical** line?

a ($^{-}3$, 1) **b** (1, $^{-}3$) **c** (2, $^{-}2$) **d** (1, 5)

e ($^{-}2$, $^{-}2$) **f** (1, 0) **g** (3, 0) **h** ($^{-}1$, 1)

2 Which of these points lie on the same **horizontal** line?

a ($^{-}4$, 4) **b** ($^{-}2$, 2) **c** (2, 0) **d** ($^{-}4$, $^{-}2$) **e** (5, $^{-}2$)

f (2, 3) **g** (0, $^{-}2$) **h** ($^{-}4$, 1) **i** (2, $^{-}2$) **j** (0, 6)

3 Find the distance between these pairs of points.

a (6, 3) and (6, 10) **b** (1, 8) and (1, 5) **c** (0, $^{-}2$) and (0, $^{-}7$)

d ($^{-}3$, 2) and ($^{-}3$, $^{-}4$) **e** (2, $^{-}4$) and ($^{-}11$, $^{-}4$) **f** ($^{-}4$, $^{-}4$) and ($^{-}4$, $^{-}14$)

4 The coordinates of three of the vertices of a square are (5, 6), ($^{-}3$, 6) and ($^{-}3$, $^{-}2$). Write down the coordinates of the fourth vertex.

5 Triangle ABC is a right-angled isosceles triangle with AC = AB. The coordinates of vertices A and B are A = ($^{-}3$, $^{-}2$) and B = ($^{-}3$, 6). Write down the two possible positions for the vertex C.

6 ABC is an isosceles triangle with AC = BC. The coordinates of vertices A and B are A = (5, 6) and B = ($^{-}1$, 6). Write down three possible positions for the vertex C.

7 ABCD is a parallelogram. The coordinates of vertices A, B and C are A = (1, 5), B = ($^{-}2$, 4) and C = ($^{-}4$, 0). Write down the coordinates of vertex D.

8 The coordinates of three of the vertices of a rectangle are ($^{-}1$, 0), ($^{-}2$, 2) and (2, 4). Write down the coordinates of the fourth vertex.

9A Multiplying and dividing by powers of 10

Example

Work out: **a** 5.68×10^5 **b** $1.74 \surd 10^3$

a $5.68 \times 10^5 = 568\,000$

b $1.74 \div 10^3 = 0.00174$

1 Work out:

a 3.6×10^3 **b** 4.1×10^4 **c** 57×10^2

d 8.5×10^0 **e** 9.3×10^5 **f** 66×10^3

g 0.08×10^3 **h** 0.0065×10^8 **i** $5.3 \surd 10^3$

j $7.8 \surd 10^2$ **k** $36.6 \surd 10^4$ **l** $476 \surd 10^6$

m $0.03 \surd 10^1$ **n** $0.5 \surd 10^0$ **o** $0.0003 \surd 10^2$

2 Work out the missing powers of 10.

a $3.61 \times 10^{\square} = 36100$ **b** $9.9 \times 10^{\square} = 990$

c $6 \times 10^{\square} = 600\,000\,000$ **d** $5.76 \times 10^{\square} = 5.76$

e $2.58 \div 10^{\square} = 0.000\,258$ **f** $8.3 \div 10^{\square} = 0.083$

g $56.4 \div 10^{\square} = 0.00564$ **h** $1.34 \div 10^{\square} = 0.000\,134$

3 Work out:

a $5.4 \times 10^2 \times 10^3$ **b** $0.01 \times 10^6 \div 10^2$

c $10^3 \times 7.2 \div 10^4$ **d** $10^6 \div 10^4 \times 9.4$

4 Find the product of 10^7 and 0.0034

5 Choose from <, > or = to complete the boxes.

a $3.2 \times 10^6 \square 32\,000 \div 10^2$

b $26 \div 10^4 \square 0.000\,026 \times 10^5$

9B Rounding to a number of decimal places

Example

Round: **a** 34.78 to 1 d.p. **b** 5.7964 to 2 d.p.

a 34.78 → 34.8 to 1 d.p.

b 5.7964 → 5.80 to 2 d.p.

1 Round correct to one decimal place (1 d.p.):

a 6.437 **b** 3.75 **c** 4.99 **d** 32.03

e 0.08 **f** 7.01 **g** 5.365 **h** 18.355

i 453.98 **j** 6.007 **k** 8.88 **l** 52.95

2 Round correct to two decimal places (2 d.p.):

a 5.362 **b** 8.444 **c** 2.035 **d** 7.777

e 15.488 **f** 4.297 **g** 10.022 **h** 45.558

i 0.3147 **j** 0.2561 **k** 0.495 **l** 0.4008

3 Round correct to the nearest whole number:

a 5.235 **b** 4.86 **c** 8.19 **d** 15.76

e 10.72 **f** 29.63 **g** 6.488 **h** 600.8

4

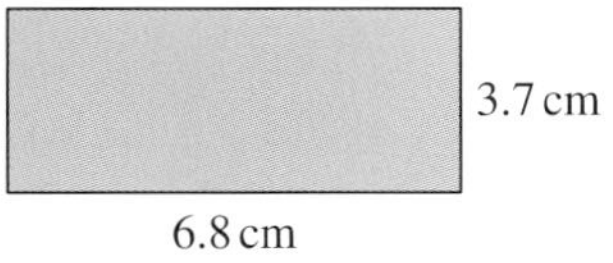

a Find the area of this rectangle.

b Write your answer to part **a** correct to 1 d.p.

5 Use a calculator to work these out. Write your answers correct to 2 d.p.

a $7\sqrt{3}$ **b** $5\sqrt{7}$ **c** $15\sqrt{11}$ **d** $20\sqrt{17}$

6 When a number is written correct to two decimal places, the answer is 4.85. Write down the smallest possible value for the number.

9C Fractions and percentages

Example

a What fraction of this shape is shaded?

b What percentage of the shape is shaded?

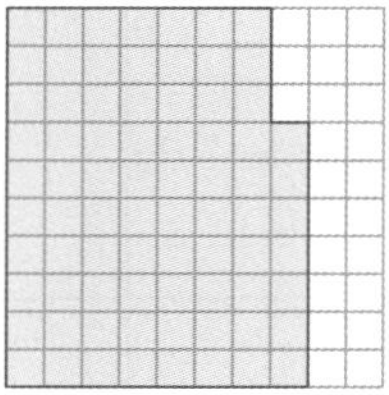

a Fraction shaded $= \frac{77}{100}$ **b** Percentage shaded = 77%

1 Write down the percentage of each shape that has been shaded.

a

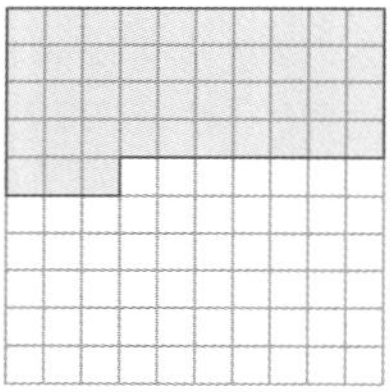

b

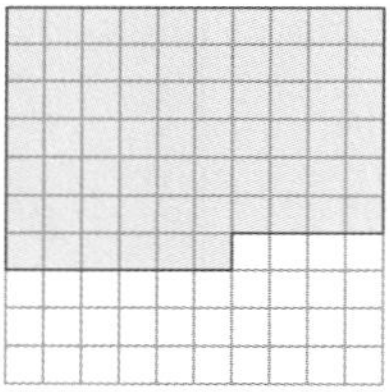

c

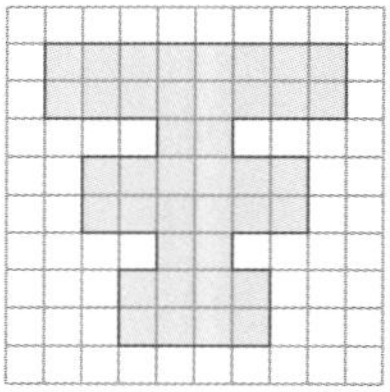

d

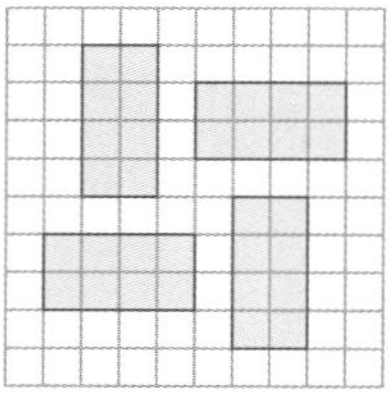

e

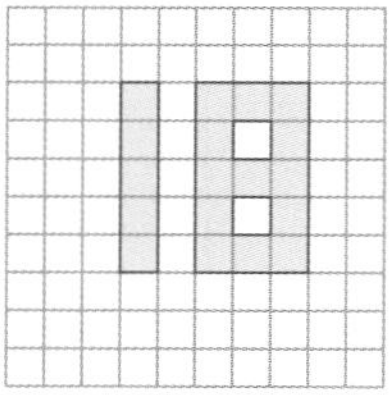

f

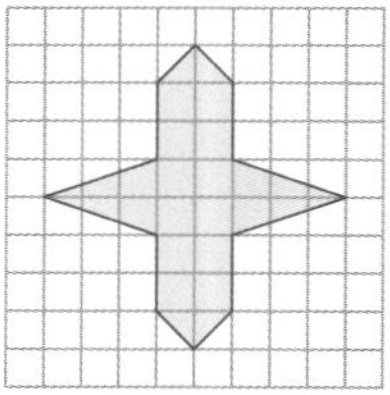

g What did you notice about your answer to part **e**?

h Draw a 10-by-10 grid. Shade 25% of the grid so that your shading shows the number 25.

2 Write these percentages as fractions.

a 43% **b** 89% **c** 77% **d** 91%

3 Write these fractions as percentages.

a $\frac{57}{100}$ **b** $\frac{9}{100}$ **c** $\frac{13}{100}$ **d** $\frac{81}{100}$ **e** $\frac{79}{100}$

9D Changing fractions to percentages

Example

There are 18 girls and 22 boys in a class.
Find the percentage of girls in this class.

18 + 22 = 40 students

÷ 2 × 5

$$\frac{18}{40} = \frac{9}{20} = \frac{45}{100} = 45\%$$

÷ 2 × 5

1 Copy and complete:

a $\frac{3}{5} = \frac{\square}{100} = \square\%$ **b** $\frac{11}{20} = \frac{\square}{100} = \square\%$ **c** $\frac{49}{50} = \frac{\square}{100} = \square\%$

d $\frac{6}{15} = \frac{\square}{5} = \frac{\square}{100} = \square\%$ **e** $\frac{26}{40} = \frac{\square}{20} = \frac{\square}{100} = \square\%$

2 Write as a percentage:

a $\frac{1}{5}$ **b** $\frac{3}{4}$ **c** $\frac{9}{10}$ **d** $\frac{17}{20}$ **e** $\frac{21}{25}$ **f** $\frac{33}{50}$

g $\frac{18}{75}$ **h** $\frac{39}{52}$ **i** $\frac{38}{40}$ **j** $\frac{33}{55}$ **k** $\frac{48}{60}$ **l** $\frac{111}{150}$

3 For each shape, find the **i** fraction shaded **ii** percentage shaded.

a

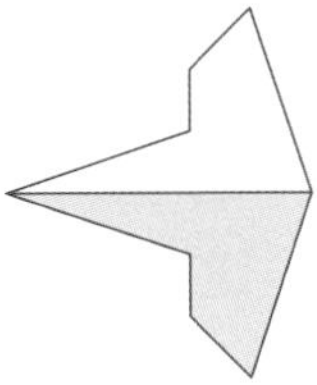

b

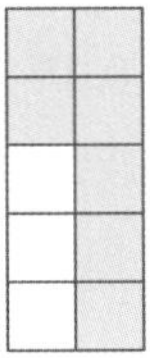

c

d

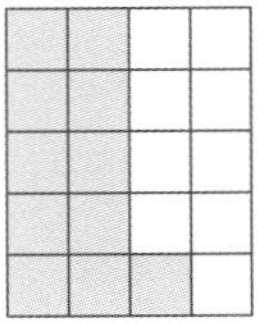

4 This table shows information about 40 people.

Find the percentage of:

a these people who have blue eyes

b these people who have dark hair

c those with fair hair who have brown eyes

d those with blue eyes who have fair hair.

	Fair hair	Dark hair
Blue eyes	12	7
Brown eyes	3	18

9E Decimals and percentages

Example

Write 0.73 as a percentage.

Method A

$0.73 = \frac{73}{100} = 73\%$

Method B

$0.73 = 0.73 \times 100\% = 73\%$

1 Copy and complete this table.

Decimal	Fraction	Percentage
0.2	$\frac{20}{100}$	20%
0.09		
		66%
0.15		
		4%
0.7		

2 Write these decimals as percentages.

a 0.53 **b** 0.07 **c** 0.7 **d** 0.39

e 0.22 **f** 0.19 **g** 0.05 **h** 0.68

i 0.035 **j** 0.008 **k** 0.021 **l** 0.4242

m 0.0516 **n** 0.0035 **o** 1.03 **p** 1.238

3 Match each decimal with the equivalent percentage.
Find the odd one out.

3.8 | 8.3% | 0.38

0.03 | 80% | 3% | 380%

0.038 | 0.83 | 3.8%

8% | 0.083 | 38% | 830%

0.08 | 8.3 | 0.8

4 Which number in each pair is larger?

a 0.02 or 19%

b $\frac{3}{8}$ or 37%

c $\frac{13}{16}$ or 83%

d $\frac{127}{16400}$ or 21%

5 Which of these diagrams have less than 35% shaded?

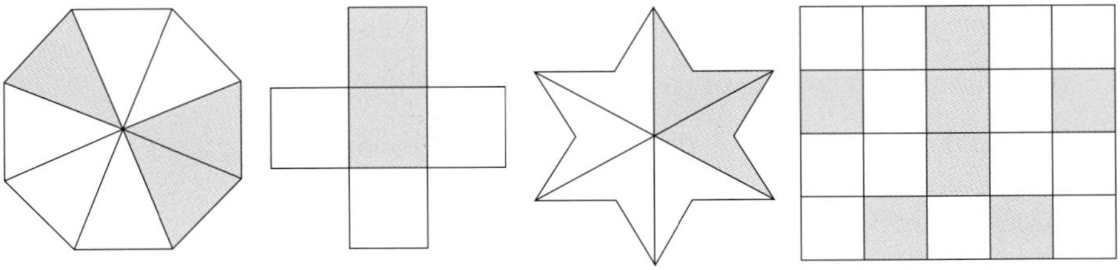

6 Write these numbers in order of size, smallest first.

$\frac{2}{3}$, 0.64, $\frac{13}{20}$, $\frac{67}{100}$, 64.5%

9F Finding percentages of amounts

Example

Find 5% of \$360

$$5\% \text{ of } \$360 = \frac{5}{100} \times 360 \quad \text{convert to fraction}$$

$$= \frac{1}{20} \times 360 \quad \text{simplify the fraction}$$

$$= 360 \div 20 \quad \text{multiplying by } \frac{1}{20} \text{ is the}$$

$$= \$18 \quad \text{same as dividing by 20}$$

1 Work out:

a 50% of \$80
b 25% of 64 m
c 10% of 130 kg
d 75% of 48 cm
e 20% of 75 litres
f 30% of \$300
g 90% of 520 g
h 5% of 460 kg
i 15% of 120 km
j 35% of \$60
k 4% of 75 eggs
l 85% of 780 bananas

2 There are 65 passengers on a bus. 80% are sitting and the rest are standing.

a Write down the percentage of the passengers who are standing.

b Work out the number of passengers who are sitting.

3 400 children chose the fruit they liked best from banana, mango, orange and pineapple. The table here shows some information about the results. Copy and complete the table.

Fruit	banana	mango	orange	pineapple
Percentage of children	38%	27%	18%	
Number of children				

4 If 9 out of 60 cars in a car park are black, what percentage are not black?

5 750 electric ovens had a safety test. 92% of the ovens passed. How many failed?

6 You may use a calculator for this question. Find:

a 0.05% of \$560
b 215% of 78 km

7 Use the digits 1 to 5, without repeating any digit, to complete this calculation.

□□% of □□□ = 51.3

9G Working with percentages

Example

22% of □ = 198
Find the missing value.

22% of □ = 198 divide both sides by 22 to find 1%
1% of □ = 9 multiply both sides by 100 to find 100%
100% of □ = 900
The missing value is 900.

1 Find the value to complete each of these sentences.

a 400% of an amount represents an increase of □%

b □% of an amount represents an increase of 560%

2 Find the missing values.

a 18% of □ = 54

b 35% of □ = 70

c 200% of □ = 380

d 450% of □ = 81

e 0.2% of □ = 4000

3 Find the value to complete each of these sentences.

a To find 200% of an amount, you multiply by □

b To find □% of an amount, you multiply by 6

c 300% of an amount is 36; to find the original amount, you divide 36 by □

d To find □% of an amount, you multiply by 2.9

4 Work out:

a 200% of 80

b 500% of 52

c 120% of 56

d 330% of 400

5 An antique clock increases in value from \$160 to \$400.
Find the value to complete each sentence:

a \$400 is □% of \$160.

b This is a □% increase in value.

6 Work out the cost of these sale items.

15% off all sale items!

a Radio \$150

b Television \$500

c Oven \$940

d Computer \$850

e Kettle \$50

f Vacuum cleaner \$250

7 Richard earns \$800 per week.
He is given a 5% pay rise.
Work out how much he now earns per week.

8 Helen buys a new car for \$15 000.
After one year, the value of the car has decreased by 35%.
Find the value of the car after one year.

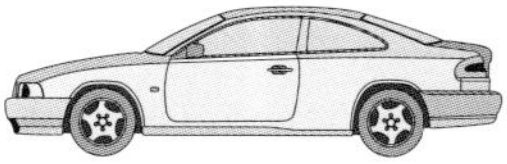

9 The cost of a holiday is reduced by 15% to \$680.
Find the original cost of the holiday.

9H–9I Comparing decimals and fractions

Example

Which fraction is greater, $\frac{3}{4}$ or $\frac{18}{25}$?

$\frac{3}{4} = \frac{75}{100} = 0.75$ and $\frac{18}{25} = \frac{72}{100} = 0.72$

$\frac{3}{4}$ is the greater fraction.

1 By writing the fractions so that they have the same common denominator, find which fraction is greater.

a $\frac{3}{4}$ or $\frac{5}{7}$ **b** $\frac{4}{5}$ or $\frac{6}{7}$ **c** $\frac{7}{8}$ or $\frac{6}{7}$

d $\frac{2}{3}$ or $\frac{4}{7}$ **e** $\frac{2}{5}$ or $\frac{3}{8}$ **f** $\frac{3}{7}$ or $\frac{4}{9}$

2 By changing each fraction to a decimal, find which fraction is greater. (You may use a calculator for parts **e** and **f**.)

a $\frac{1}{4}$ or $\frac{3}{10}$ **b** $\frac{16}{25}$ or $\frac{3}{4}$ **c** $\frac{17}{20}$ or $\frac{19}{25}$

d $\frac{19}{50}$ or $\frac{17}{20}$ **e** $\frac{4}{7}$ or $\frac{5}{11}$ **f** $\frac{7}{12}$ or $\frac{74}{125}$

3 $\frac{5}{7}$ 0.79 $\frac{2}{3}$ 0.83 $\frac{8}{11}$ $\frac{14}{17}$

Which of these are greater than $\frac{4}{5}$? (You may use a calculator.)

4 $\frac{3}{4}$ $\frac{2}{5}$ $\frac{1}{2}$ $\frac{5}{8}$ $\frac{7}{10}$ $\frac{17}{20}$

Write these fractions in order of size, starting with the lowest.

5 Are these statements true or false?

a $\frac{5}{8} < \frac{5}{9}$ **b** $\frac{6}{11} > \frac{2}{3}$ **c** $\frac{4}{5} < \frac{8}{9}$

6 Write the following fractions in order of size, using inequality signs like this:

□ < □ < □ < □

$\frac{2}{3}, \frac{3}{5}, \frac{7}{12}, \frac{13}{20}$

9J Adding and subtracting decimals

Example

Work out: **a** $2.05 + 3 + 1.78$ **b** $6.4 - 2.17$

a

```
  2.05
+ 3
+ 1.78
  ----
  6.83
  1
```

b

```
   3 1
  6.40
- 2.17
  ----
  4.23
```

1 Work out:

a $4.3 + 2.4$ **b** $5.2 + 1.8$ **c** $6.5 + 2.7$ **d** $6 + 3.9$

e $2.3 + 7$ **f** $0.02 + 6.4$ **g** $3.98 + 4.6$ **h** $5.77 + 4.28$

2 Work out:

a $5 + 0.5 + 0.27$ **b** $2.3 + 9 + 1.03$ **c** $0.05 + 0.28 + 4$

d $20 + 1.9 + 0.22$ **e** $17.2 + 156 + 0.74$ **f** $0.002 + 86 + 0.96$

3 Find the total cost of a book for \$8.49, an album for \$15 and a pen for \$5.89.

4 Find the odd one out:

$3.487 + 5.963 + 2.09$	$4.9 + 3.077 + 3.553$	$8 + 0.998 + 2.532$

5 The times for the four runners in a 4×100 metre relay team were:

11.47 s	11.58 s	12.24 s	11.08 s

a Find their total time.

b The previous club record was 47.03 seconds.
By how much did they better the record?

6 The numbers in the squares are the sum of the numbers in the circles.
Find the missing numbers.

a

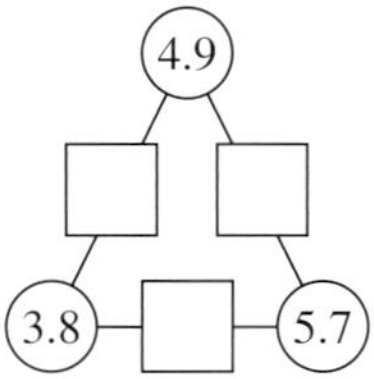

b

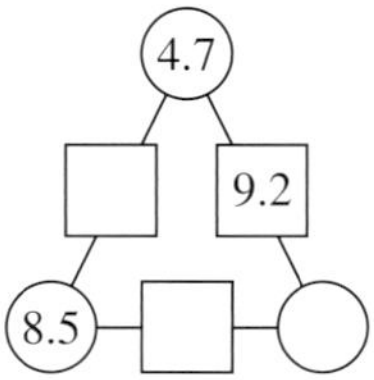

c

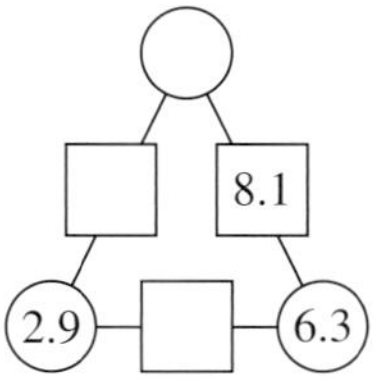

7 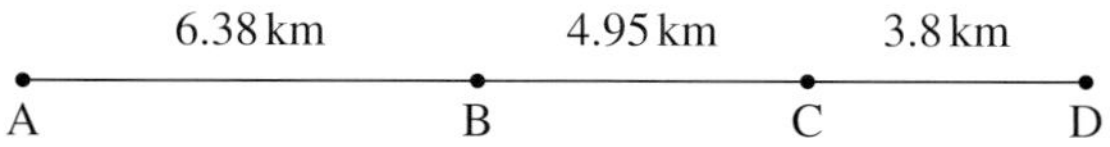

Find the distance between A and D.

8 Work out:

a $38.4 - 12$ **b** $9.2 - 2.8$ **c** $7 - 0.6$

d $15 - 2.3$ **e** $15.3 - 6.7$ **f** $4.7 - 2.08$

g $21 - 0.39$ **h** $12.68 - 4.004$ **i** $7.8 - 5.68$

j $80 - 8.47$ **k** $17.3 - 6.48$ **l** $20.3 - 5.998$

9 Find the odd one out.

$5.249 - 3.184$	$18.605 - 15.64$	$3.631 - 1.566$

10 Raju bought a book for \$9.35 and a pack of pens for \$7.89.
He paid with a \$20 bill.
How much change did he receive?

11 Helen and Anya took part in a long jump competition.
Helen jumped 6.45 metres and Anya jumped 5.87 metres.
How much further did Helen jump than Anya?

12 **a** By rounding each number to the nearest integer, estimate the answers to these calculations.

i $^{-}4.28 + 6.57$ **ii** $^{-}2.77 - {}^{-}3.8$ **iii** $^{-}1.72 - 3.98 - {}^{-}1.342$

b Now work out the exact answers and compare them to your estimates.

13 Find the missing numbers.

a
$$\begin{array}{r} 9.\square 3 \\ -\ \square.45 \\ \hline 6.88 \\ \hline \end{array}$$

b
$$\begin{array}{r} \square.4\square \\ -\ 5.\square 2 \\ \hline 2.74 \\ \hline \end{array}$$

c
$$\begin{array}{r} 4.29\square \\ -\ \square.6\square 7 \\ \hline 1.\square 46 \\ \hline \end{array}$$

14 Work out:

a $12.6 + {}^{-}6.35$ **b** $5.8 - {}^{-}4.88$

c $^{-}12.6 + 7.21$ **d** $5.2 + {}^{-}8.9$

e $8.4 - 10.2 + 9.65$ **f** $^{-}8.9 + 3.3 + 5.07$

g $^{-}4.9 + 8.14 + {}^{-}2.65$ **h** $^{-}5.8 + {}^{-}5.8 - {}^{-}5.8$

9K Multiplying decimals

Example

Work out 2.81×3

First do the calculation without decimal places.

$$\begin{array}{r} 281 \\ \times\ 3 \\ \hline 843 \\ \hline {\scriptstyle 2} \end{array}$$

There are 2 d.p. in the product so there will be 2 d.p. in the answer.

$2.\underline{81} \times 3 = 8.\underline{43}$

1 Work out:

a 0.3×2 **b** 0.5×9 **c** 7×0.2

d 0.6×8 **e** 6×0.4 **f** 0.8×3

g 0.07×7 **h** 6×0.05 **i** 0.04×8

j 2×0.09 **k** 0.04×5 **l** 8×0.007

2 Work out using a quick method:

a $5 \times 0.9 \times 0.2$ **b** $8 \times 0.4 \times 5$ **c** $0.7 \times 0.5 \times 6$

3 Given $5 \times 0.03 = 0.15$, work out:

a $0.15 \surd 5$ **b** $0.15 \surd 0.03$

4 Work out:

a 0.14×2 **b** 2×0.36 **c** 0.43×3

d 5.24×8 **e** 6.47×4 **f** 7.31×8

g 23.4×6 **h** 8×31.25 **i** 43.16×7

j 28.94×9 **k** 8.09×5 **l** 4×103.56

5 **a** Find the cost of 4 kg of cheese at \$21.85 per kilogram.

b Find the cost of 3.4 kg of biscuits at \$9 per kilogram.

c Find the cost of 5 litres of paint at \$7.95 per litre.

(6) Copy and complete:

a $7.4 \times \square = 44.4$ **b** $5.86 \times \square = 41.02$ **c** $9.15 \times \square = 73.2$

9L Dividing decimals

Example

Work out 85.2 √ 6

$$\begin{array}{r} 1\,4.\,2 \\ 6\overline{)8^{2}5.^{1}2} \end{array}$$

1 Work out:

a 19.6 √ 7	**b** 11.4 √ 6	**c** 19.5 √ 5	**d** 92.8 √ 8
e 0.805 √ 7	**f** 4.56 √ 4	**g** 0.146 √ 2	**h** 9.42 √ 3
i 0.375 √ 5	**j** 0.0522 √ 6	**k** 0.654 √ 2	**l** 1.944 √ 6
m 0.228 √ 4	**n** 5.58 √ 6	**o** 5.74 √ 7	**p** 1.872 √ 8
q 75.2 √ 4	**r** 0.3 √ 8	**s** 1.3 √ 4	**t** 0.22 √ 5

2 The cost of 7 pencils is \$6.23.
Find the cost of one pencil.

3 The cost of 8 pens is \$19.92.
Find the cost of one pen.

4 The cost of 5 litres of oil is \$18.20.
Find the cost of one litre of oil.

5 Which is the better value?

8 kg of bananas
for \$19.60
OR
7 kg of bananas
for \$17.22

6 Given $0.132 \div 4 = 0.033$, work out:

a 0.033×4 **b** 0.132 √ 0.033

7 Copy and complete:

a $5.22 \div \square = 1.74$ **b** $0.216 \div \square = 0.054$ **c** $1.8 \div \square = 0.36$

10A Two-way tables

Example

This table shows information about 80 applicants for a job.

	Can drive	Cannot drive
Computer-skilled	26	9
Not computer-skilled	38	7

a Find the total number of applicants who can drive.

b Find the total number of applicants who are not computer-skilled.

a Number of applicants who can drive = 26 + 38 = 64

b Number of applicants who are not computer-skilled = 38 + 7 = 45

1 This table shows information about how Class 8B travel to school.

	Walk	Cycle	Bus
Girls	5	3	7
Boys	6	4	6

a How many girls are in Class 8B?

b How many students cycle to school?

c How many students are there altogether in Class 8B?

2 This diagram shows black, grey and white shapes. Each shape is a circle or a square.

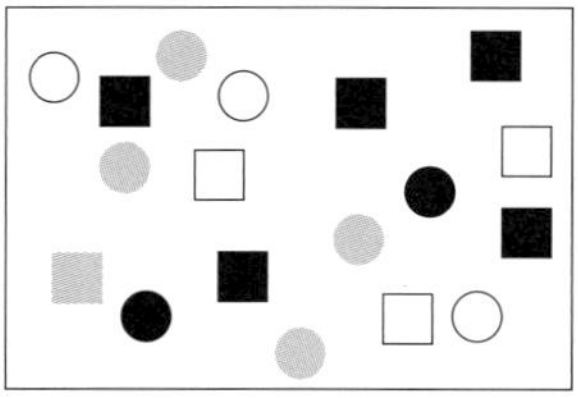

Copy and complete this two-way table to record the types of shapes in the diagram.

	Black	Grey	White	Total
Circle	2			
Square		1		
Total				

3 This table shows information about members of a tennis club.
Copy and complete the table.

	League 1	League 2	Total
Female	12		
Male	8		43
Total			87

4 Each of the 200 students in a school must attend one lunchtime club.
They have a choice of Sports Club or Drama Club.
This table shows information about the number of students attending each club.
Copy and complete the table.

	Sports	Drama	Total
Girls	62		
Boys		41	95
Total			200

5 This table shows information about the number of students in years 12 and 13 in a school. Copy and complete the table.

	Year group		Total
	Year 12	Year 13	
Boys	253		
Girls		245	
Total		479	969

10B Presenting data

Example

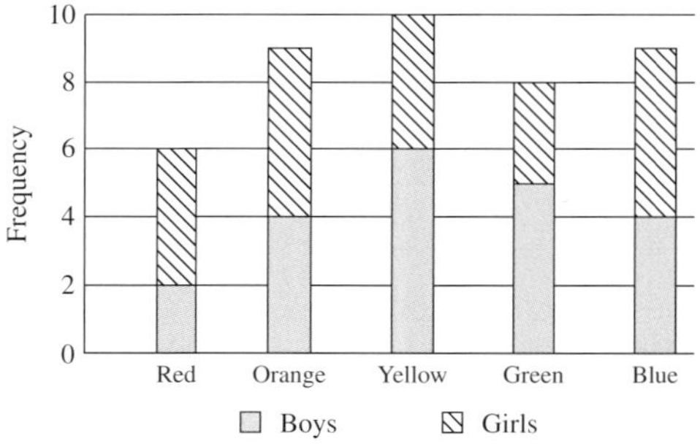

This compound bar chart shows information about the favourite colours of a group of children.

a Which colour is most popular?

b What is the boys' favourite colour?

c What is the girls' least favourite colour?

d How many children were in the survey?

---

a The most popular colour is yellow.

b The boys' favourite colour is yellow.

c The girls' least favourite colour is green.

d The total number of children = $6 + 9 + 10 + 8 + 9 = 42$

1 This dual bar chart shows the number of kilometres that Allan and Brendan ran on five days in one week.

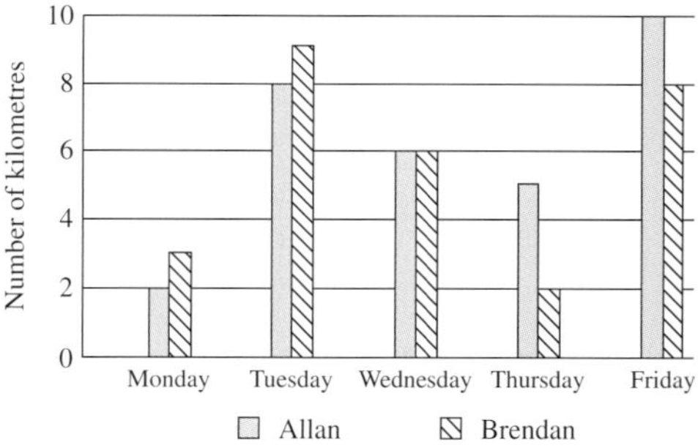

a On which two days did Allan run farther than Brendan?

b Who ran farther in total over the five days?

c On Saturday, Allan runs 8 km. How far must Brendan run on Saturday so that the total number of kilometres that he runs from Monday to Saturday is the same as the total number of kilometres that Allan runs from Monday to Saturday?

2 30 students in Year 7 and Year 8 are asked which flavour of ice cream they prefer, vanilla, chocolate or strawberry.
This table shows the results.

	Vanilla	Chocolate	Strawberry
Year 7	8	15	7
Year 8	10	8	12

a Draw a dual bar chart to show this information.

b Explain how the dual bar chart is an improvement on the two-way table for showing this information.

3 Aisha runs a bike shop. Her sales of girls' bikes and boys' bikes over five days are shown in this table.

	Monday	Tuesday	Wednesday	Thursday	Friday
Boys' bikes	4	5	7	6	10
Girls' bikes	3	9	9	12	12

a Draw a compound bar chart to show this information.

b Describe the trend in the total number of sales of bikes over these five days. Explain how the compound bar chart shows this.

10C Summary statistics

Example

This frequency table shows the test marks of 20 students.

Mark	7	8	9	10
Frequency	4	9	5	2

a Calculate the mean mark.
b Find the modal test mark.
c Find the median test mark.
d Find the range of test marks.

---

a Mean $= \frac{(7\times4)+(8\times9)+(9\times5)+(10\times2)}{20}$

$= \frac{28+72+45+20}{20}$

$= \frac{165}{20}$

$= 8.25$

b Mode = test mark that occurs most often = 8

c Median $= \frac{20+1}{2}$ th value = 10.5th value = 8

d Range = largest value − smallest value
$= 10 - 7 = 3$

1 This table shows the number of pets owned by 20 people.

Number of pets	Frequency	Number of pets × frequency
0	5	$0 \times 5 = 0$
1	8	$1 \times 8 =$
2	6	
3	1	
Total		

a Copy and complete the table. Find the mean number of pets.

b Find the modal number of pets.

c Find the median number of pets.

d Find the range of the number of pets.

2 This frequency table shows the number of suitcases belonging to each of 20 air passengers.

Number of suitcases	0	1	2	3
Frequency	1	10	7	2

a Find the mean number of suitcases.

b Find the modal number of suitcases.

c Find the median.

d Find the range.

3 This table shows the scores of 50 participants in a quiz.

Quiz score	6	7	8	9	10
Frequency	9	12	11	10	8

a Find the mean quiz score.

b Find the mode.

c Find the median.

d Find the range.

4 This table shows the number of goals scored in 40 football matches.

Number of goals	0	1	2	3	4
Frequency	5	11	15	6	3

a Find the mean number of goals scored.

b Find the mode.

c Find the median.

d Find the range.

5 This bar chart shows the number of eggs found in 13 nests.

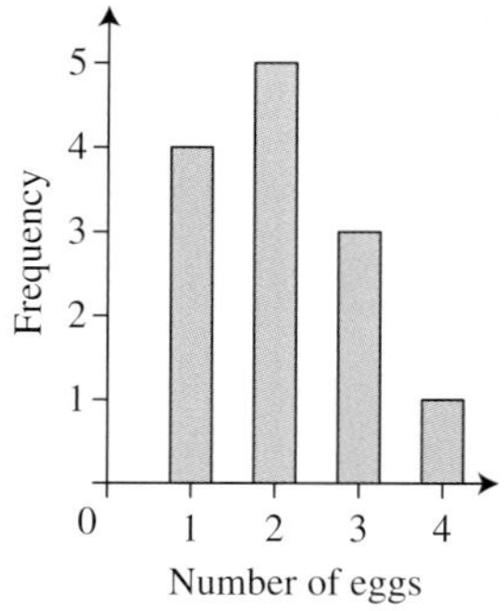

a Write down, in order, the number of eggs in each of the 13 nests.

b Write down the modal number of eggs.

c Find the median number of eggs.

d Calculate the mean number of eggs.

6 30 students in a class were asked how many pencils they had in their pencil case. The results are shown in this bar chart.

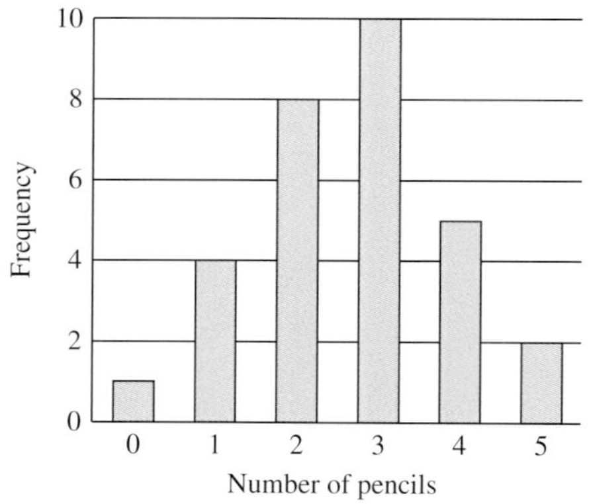

a Find the mean number of pencils in a pencil case.

b Find the mode.

c Find the median.

d Find the range.

10D Using the most appropriate average

Example

The number of goals scored by each of ten football players in a season is shown here.

3	8	7	9	1
2	52	11	8	8

a Find the mean number of goals.

b Find the modal number of goals.

c Find the median number of goals.

d Explain why the mean is not a good representative value for this data set.

---

a Mean $= \dfrac{3+8+7+9+1+2+52+11+8+8}{10}$

$= \dfrac{109}{10} = 10.9$

b Mode = 8

c Number of goals in order: 1 2 3 7 8 8 8 9 11 52

Median = middle value = 8

d The mean has been distorted by the large number of goals scored by one player.

1 The amounts of pocket money received by ten children are:

\$9 \$10 \$10 \$10 \$12 \$14 \$15 \$15 \$16 \$50

a Find:

i the mode

ii the median

iii the mean

b Which of the three averages best represents the children's pocket money? Give a reason for your answer.

c Write down the range for the amount of pocket money.

2 A shopkeeper records the sizes of the dresses sold in one week.

Dress size	Frequency
8	6
10	15
12	34
14	22
16	13
18	10

a Find the mean.

b Find the mode.

c Find the median.

d Which of the averages gives the most useful information for the shopkeeper?

3 This table shows the amount of rainfall (in cm) in January for a city over a five-year period.

Year	2017	2018	2019	2020	2021
Rainfall (cm)	13.9	22.4	11.2	12.4	10.9

a Find the mean.

b Find the mode.

c Find the median.

d Jameela wants to visit this city in January. Which average do you think would be most useful to her? Explain your answer.

4 The mean of 4, 7, 9 and x is the same as the mean of 7, 8, 9, 9 and 10. Find the value of x.

5 Roberto takes examinations in mathematics, English and science.

Maths 68%
English 74%
Science

a Calculate his mean mark in mathematics and English.

b Roberto's science mark decreases his mean mark to 66%. What is his science mark?

10E Representing and interpreting data

Example

This bar chart shows information about the average price of a house in a region.

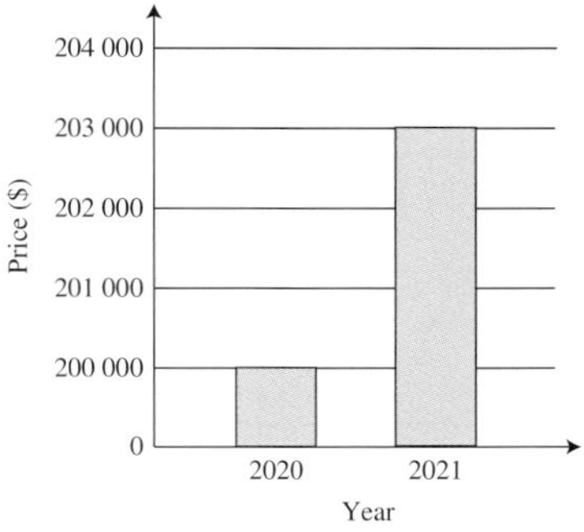

a Explain why the bar chart is misleading.

b Draw the bar chart correctly.

a The scale on the vertical axis is not linear. This makes the chart appear as if house prices have quadrupled.

b

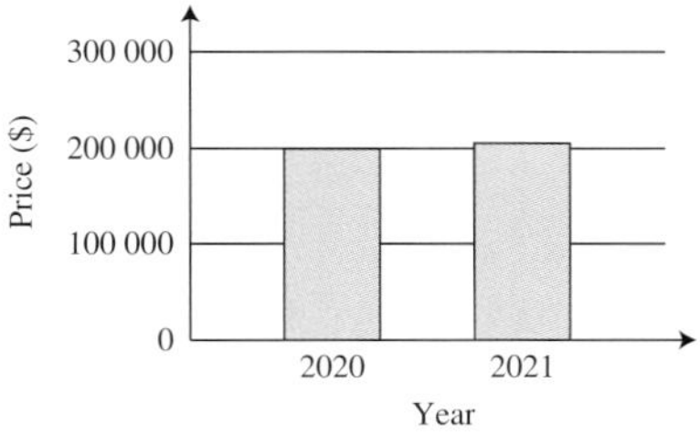

1 Danuta owns an ice-cream shop. She wants to know if there is a relationship between the number of ice creams sold and the midday temperature outside. This table shows the data that she collected.

Temperature (°C)	15	24	29	26	18	20	23	27	17
Number of ice creams	50	80	93	85	60	66	72	92	55

a What type of graph or chart should she draw?

b Draw the graph or chart and describe the relationship shown between temperature and ice creams sold.

2 This table shows the average monthly temperatures in a city from January to July.

a Draw a line graph to show this information.

b Ricardo says that the line graph shows that global warming is really happening. Do you think Ricardo is correct? Give reasons for your answer.

Month	Temperature (°C)
January	5.2
February	7.8
March	10.1
April	16.1
May	21.5
June	26.8
July	29.4

11A Simplifying ratios

Example

Write each ratio in its simplest form.

a 64 : 38 **b** 7 : 0.3 **c** $\frac{2}{5} : \frac{7}{10}$

a 64 : 38 ÷ 2 ÷ 2 → 32 : 19

b 7 : 0.3 × 10 × 10 → 70 : 3

c $\frac{2}{5} : \frac{7}{10}$ × 10 × 10 → 4 : 7

1 Write each ratio in its simplest form.

a 3 : 6 **b** 7 : 14 **c** 8 : 4 **d** 27 : 18

e 6 : 8 **f** 35 : 20 **g** 28 : 20 **h** 50 : 20

i 15 : 10 **j** 64 : 24 **k** 49 : 63 **l** 50 : 250

m 21 : 15 **n** 32 : 36 **o** 231 : 111 **p** 392 : 413

2 Match equivalent pairs of ratios. Find the odd one out.

7 : 14	12 : 9	3 : 1	20 : 24	
5 : 6	52 : 13	6 : 7	21 : 18	1 : 2
4 : 3	42 : 14	7 : 6	4 : 1	

3 Write each ratio in its simplest form.

a 12 : 18 : 24 **b** 35 : 14 : 7 **c** 96 : 36 : 60 **d** 400 : 50 : 250

4 Write each ratio in its simplest form.

a 0.3 : 2 **b** 0.8 : 5 **c** 7 : 1.3 **d** 4.6 : 8.4

e 0.6 : 0.3 : 0.7 **f** 0.5 : 4 : 1.5 **g** 1.2 : 0.8 : 4 **h** 5.5 : 8 : 2.5

5 By first writing the fractions with a common denominator, give each ratio in its simplest form:

a $\frac{1}{4}:\frac{1}{2}$ **b** $\frac{2}{3}:\frac{1}{6}$ **c** $\frac{3}{5}:\frac{7}{10}$ **d** $\frac{2}{7}:\frac{1}{5}$

e $\frac{7}{8}:\frac{1}{4}$ **f** $\frac{1}{9}:\frac{2}{3}$ **g** $\frac{7}{10}:\frac{2}{5}$ **h** $\frac{2}{11}:\frac{1}{2}$

i $\frac{3}{4}:\frac{2}{3}$ **j** $\frac{3}{8}:\frac{4}{7}$ **k** $\frac{7}{12}:\frac{3}{4}$ **l** $\frac{5}{12}:\frac{7}{8}$

6 Write each ratio in its simplest form.

a $\frac{1}{2}:6$ **b** $8:\frac{1}{3}$ **c** $1.2:\frac{1}{4}$ **d** $\frac{3}{5}:\frac{1}{2}$

e $0.8:15\%:\frac{1}{4}$ **f** $\frac{1}{2}:\frac{1}{3}:\frac{1}{4}$ **g** $3.2:\frac{1}{5}$ **h** $\frac{1}{3}:\frac{5}{6}:\frac{8}{9}$

11B Dividing a quantity in a given ratio

Example

Share 96 sweets between Anna, Ben and Chan in the ratio 2 : 7 : 3

$2 + 7 + 3 = 12$ parts
1 part $= 96 \div 12 = 8$
Anna receives $2 \times 8 = 16$ sweets
Ben receives $7 \times 8 = 56$ sweets
Chan receives $3 \times 8 = 24$ sweets

1 

These pens are to be shared between Raju and Nadia in the ratio 2 : 1.

a How many pens does Raju receive?

b How many pens does Nadia receive?

2 There are 35 chocolates in a box.
The ratio of dark chocolates to milk chocolates is 2 : 5.
Work out the number of dark and milk chocolates.

3 In a carton of juice, 22% is mango juice and the rest is apple juice.

a Write down the ratio of mango juice to apple juice.

b Work out the amount of each type of juice in a 1-litre carton.

4 Divide:

a \$120 in the ratio 2 : 1

b 750 cm in the ratio 2 : 3

c 3.42 kg in the ratio 1 : 2

d 48 minutes in the ratio 7 : 5

5 In this question, change the units to make the calculations easier.
Divide:

a 2 hours in the ratio 9 : 1

b 2 weeks in the ratio 2 : 5

c 0.6 litre in the ratio 7 : 5

d 750 cm in the ratio 2 : 3

6 Find two numbers that are in the ratio 17 : 21 and have a sum of 228.

7 The three angles of a triangle are in the ratio 5 : 3 : 1.
Work out the size of each angle.

11C Proportion

Example

Mona and Danny invest money in a business in the ratio 4 : 3.
If Mona invests \$652, how much does Danny invest?

$\$652 \div 4 = \$163$
Danny invests $3 \times \$163 = \$489$

1 The ratio of cows to sheep on a farm is 5 : 7.
There are 45 cows.
How many sheep are there?

2 The ratio of tourists to locals on a bus is 3 : 2.
There are 54 locals.
How many tourists are there?

3 **a** If 5 pineapples cost \$6.35, what is the cost of 3 pineapples?

b If 6 cartons of milk cost \$8.70, what do 5 cartons of milk cost?

c If 15 m of material costs \$145.20, what does 7 m of material cost?

4 If 2.5 litres of paint covers 50 m^2, what area would 12 litres of paint cover?

5 A machine fills 500 bottles in 3 minutes.
At this same rate, how long would the machine take to fill 900 bottles?

6 The ratio of adults to children on a train is 8 : 3.
There are 54 children on the train.
Find the total number of people on the train.

7 At a football match, the ratio of 'home' fans to 'away' fans is 9 : 2.
There are 2565 'home' fans.
Find the number of 'away' fans.

8 A length of string is cut into two pieces in the ratio 4 : 3.
The longer piece is 96 cm long.
Find the length of the shorter piece.

9 Jameelah is exactly 8 years older than Alia.
The ratio of their ages is 9 : 7.
How old is Alia?

11D Comparing using ratios

Example

5 cakes cost \$12.35
8 cakes cost \$19.60
Which is the better value?

Cake : dollars		Cake : dollars	
5 : 12.35		8 : 19.60	
$\div 5$ ↓	↓ $\div 5$	$\div 8$ ↓	↓ $\div 8$
1 : 2.47		1 : 2.45	

The price per cake is less for the 8 cakes, thus 8 cakes for \$19.60 is the better value.

1 5 peaches cost \$3.05
2 peaches cost \$1.24
Which is the better value?

2 Which deal is the better value?

SPECIAL DEALS

7 PLANTS FOR \$17.22

12 PLANTS FOR \$29.64

3 A $\frac{3}{4}$ kg box of chocolates costs \$5.94

A $\frac{1}{2}$ kg box of chocolates costs \$3.92

Which is the better value?

4 Ronny scored 56 goals in 80 football matches.
Zak scored 75 goals in 100 matches.
Which football player had the higher scoring rate?

5 Two tins of green paint are made by mixing blue and yellow paint, in the proportions shown in the table.

	Blue : Yellow
Tin A	5 : 3
Tin B	8 : 5

Use the unitary method to find which tin contains a higher proportion of blue paint.

6 Nathan makes a drink using squash and water in the ratio 3 : 22.
Jane makes a drink using squash and water in the ratio 5 : 36.
Use the unitary method to find whose drink is stronger.

7 Which size bottle of washing-up liquid is the best value?

0.4 litres
$2.56

0.75 litres
$5.10

1.2 litres
$7.38

12A Looking for patterns

Example

Pattern 1	Pattern 2	Pattern 3	Pattern 4
5 dots	8 dots	11 dots	14 dots

Write down a rule connecting the pattern number and the number of dots.

The rule connecting the pattern number and the number of dots is:
number of dots $= (3 \times$ pattern number$) + 2$

1 For each of these sequences, write down:

i the number of dots in the 5th pattern

ii the number of dots in the 50th pattern

iii a rule connecting the pattern number and the number of dots

a

Pattern number	1	2	3	4	5
	• •	•• ••	••• •••	•••• ••••	?
Number of dots	2	4	6	8	?

b

Pattern number	1	2	3	4	5
	•• •••	••• •••	••• ••••	•••• ••••	?
Number of dots	5	6	7	8	?

c

Pattern number	1	2	3	4	5
		• •	•• ••	••• •••	?
Number of dots	0	2	4	6	?

2

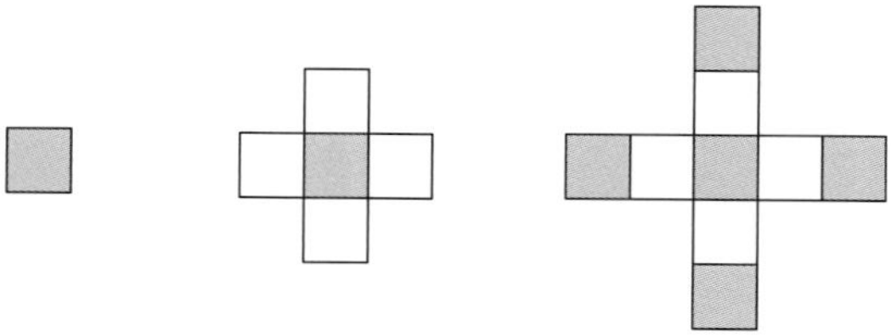

Pattern 1   Pattern 2   Pattern 3

a Write down the number of squares in:

i each of these patterns

ii the next pattern in the sequence

iii the 20th pattern in the sequence

b Write down a rule connecting the pattern number and the number of squares.

12B Number sequences

Example

Write down the next two terms in these sequences.

a 8, 14, 20, 26, 32, … **b** 14, 11, 8, 5, 2, …

a The terms increase by 6, so the next two terms are 38 and 44.

b The terms decrease by 3, so the next two terms are $^{-}1$ and $^{-}4$.

1 Write down the next two terms in each of these sequences.

a 7, 11, 15, 19, 23, … **b** 2, 8, 14, 20, 26, …

c 4, 7, 10, 13, 16, … **d** 11, 13, 15, 17, 19, …

e 30, 28, 26, 24, 22, … **f** 62, 57, 52, 47, 42, …

g 14, 11, 8, 5, 2, … **h** 5, 3, 1, $^{-}1$, $^{-}3$, …

i $^{-}30$, $^{-}26$, $^{-}22$, $^{-}18$, $^{-}14$, … **j** 6.5, 5, 3.5, 2, 0.5, …

2 For each of the sequences in question **1**, write down:

i the term-to-term rule **ii** the tenth term

3 Find the missing numbers in these sequences.

a 62, □, 72, 77, □, 87, … **b** □, 18, 21, 24, □, 30, …

c 8, 15, □, □, 36, 43, … **d** $^{-}5$, □, $^{-}1$, □, 3, □, …

4 Write down the next two terms in each of these sequences.

a 2, 3, 5, 8, 12, … **b** 2, 4, 8, 16, 32, …

c 1000, 100, 10, 1, 0.1, … **d** 160, 80, 40, 20, 10, …

e 2, 3, 5, 8, 13, … **f** 1, 3, 9, 27, 81, …

g 14, 11, 8, 5, 2, … **h** 7, 4, 11, 15, 26, …

i $^{-}20$, $^{-}19$, $^{-}17$, $^{-}14$, $^{-}10$, … **j** 6.5, 7, 8, 9.5, 11.5, …

5

38	43	50	13	28	23
15	18	29	22	33	36

These cards can be used to make two sequences, each with six terms.
The term-to-term rule for one of the sequences is 'add 7'.
Find the term-to-term rule for the other sequence.

12C The *n*th term

Example

Find the nth term for the sequence 7, 8, 9, 10, 11, ...

First term is	$1+6$
Second term is	$2+6$
Third term is	$3+6$
Fourth term is	$4+6$
Fifth term is	$5+6$
nth term is	$n+6$

1 The position-to-term rule for a sequence is $n + 4$.

a Find the 20th term.

b Find the 100th term.

2 The position-to-term rule for a sequence is $n - 7$.

a Find the 10th term.

b Find the 50th term.

3 The position-to-term rule for a sequence is $4n$.

a Find the 40th term.

b One term has value 76. Which term is it?

4 Find the nth term of each of these sequences.

a 2, 3, 4, 5, 6, …

b 7, 8, 9, 10, 11, …

c 5, 6, 7, 8, 9, …

d $^{-}3, ^{-}2, ^{-}1, 0, 1$, …

e 4, 8, 12, 16, 20, …

f 6, 12, 18, 24, 30, …

g $^{-}2, ^{-}4, ^{-}6, ^{-}8, ^{-}10$, ...

h $^{-}7, ^{-}14, ^{-}21, ^{-}28, ^{-}35$, …

5 The nth term of a sequence is $n - 5$.
How many negative terms are there in the sequence?

6 The position-to-term rule for a sequence is $7 - 3n$.
Write down the first five terms of this sequence.

7 The position-to-term rule for a sequence is $5n - 2$.

a Find the 40th term.

b One term has value 83. Which term is it?

12D Functions

Example

Using the numbers 1, 2, 3, 4, and 5 for the inputs, draw a mapping diagram for the function 'multiply by 6 and subtract 5'.

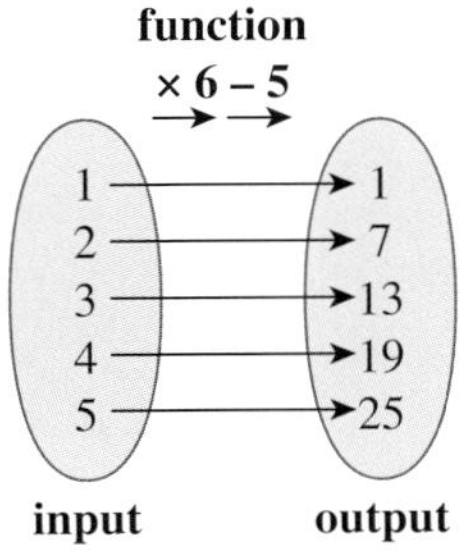

Copy and complete these mapping diagrams.

1

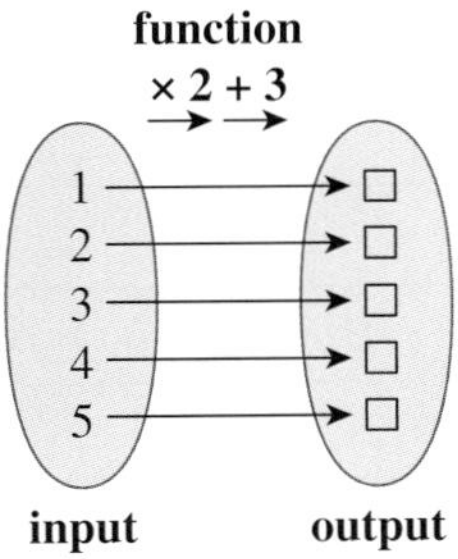

2

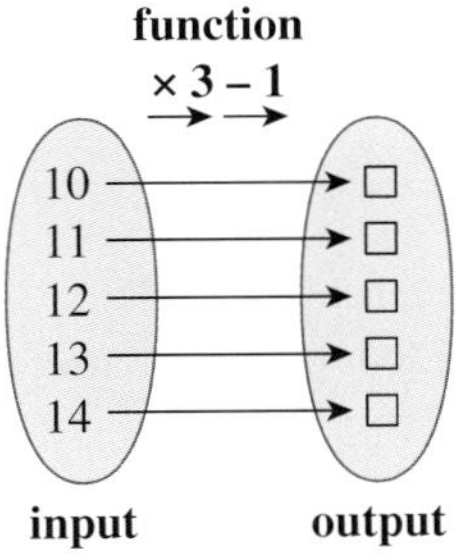

3

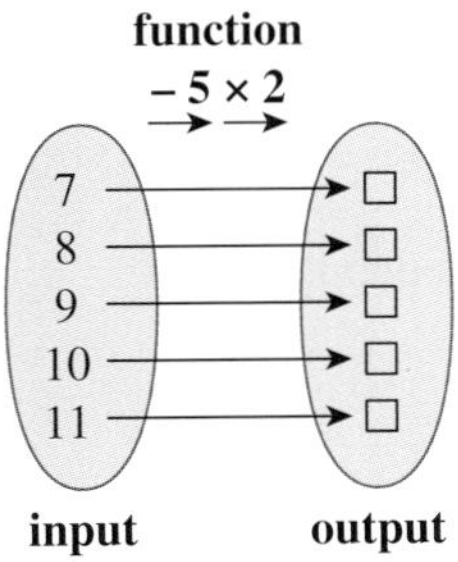

4

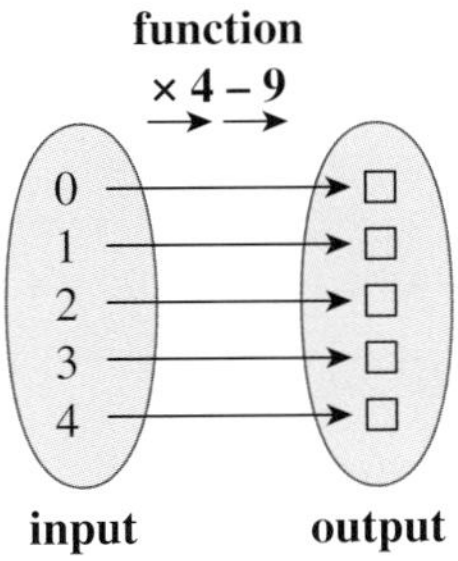

5

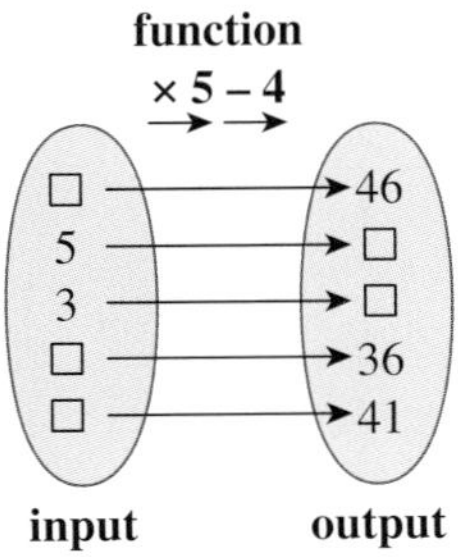

6

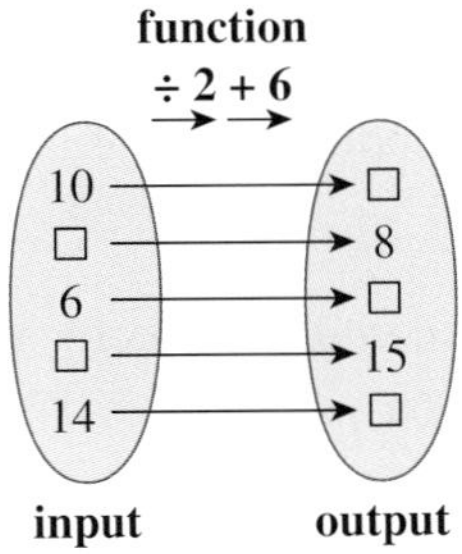

12E Graphs of linear functions

Example

Draw the graph of $y = x - 1$.

First make a table of values.

x	0	1	2	3
y	$^{-}1$	0	1	2

Then plot the points on a pair of axes.

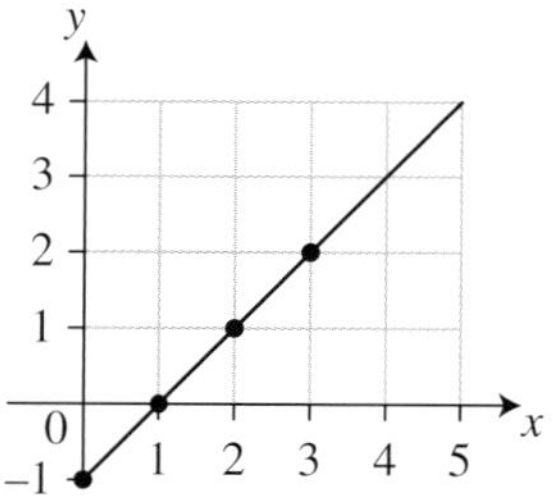

1 Copy and complete the table for $y = 2x$.
Draw the graph of $y = 2x$, choosing suitable axes.

x	0	1	2	3
y				

2 Copy and complete the table for $y = x + 1$.
Draw the graph of $y = x + 1$, choosing suitable axes.

x	0	2	4	6
y				

3 Copy and complete the table for $y = x - 2$.
Draw the graph of $y = x - 2$, choosing suitable axes.

x	0	2	4	6
y				

4 One of these points does not lie on the line $y = x + 4$. Which one is it?

($^{-}3$, 1) (10, 6) ($^{-}2$, 2) (0, 4)

5 Copy and complete the table for $y = 2x + 3$.
Draw the graph of $y = 2x + 3$, choosing suitable axes.

x	0	1	2	3
y				

6 Copy and complete these coordinate pairs for $y = 3x + 2$.

(4, □) (2, □) (0, □) (3, □)

7 Copy and complete these coordinate pairs for $y = \frac{1}{2}x - 2$.

(4, □) (10, □) (0, □) ($^{-}4$, □)

8 Which of these points does not lie on the line $y = 4x - 5$?

(2, 3) (0, $^{-}1$) (4, 11) (7, 23)

12F Horizontal and vertical lines

Example

Draw the graph of $y = 2$.

Every point on the line $y = 2$ will have a y-coordinate of 2.
Some of these points are: (3, 2), (1, 2), ($^-3$, 2), (2, 2).
Plot the points on a pair of axes and join with a straight line.

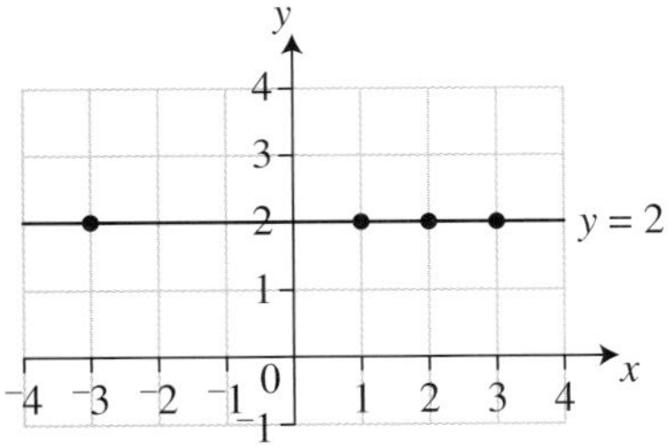

1 Plot the points (3, 4), (1, 4), ($^-3$, 4), (2, 4) and ($^-1$, 4) on a pair of axes. What is the equation of the straight line that passes through these five points?

2 Plot the points ($^-3$, 5), ($^-3$, $^-3$), ($^-3$, 1), ($^-3$, $^-5$) and ($^-3$, 4) on a pair of axes. What is the equation of the straight line that passes through these five points?

3 Write down the equations of the lines A, B, C, D, E and F.

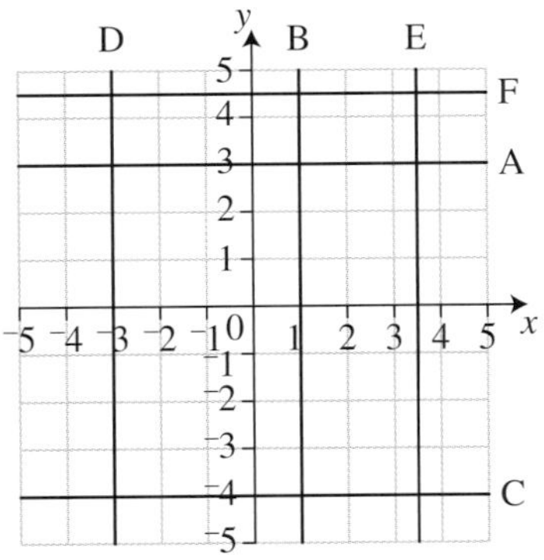

4 For each set of coordinates, write down an equation for the line that passes through all of them.

a ($^-2$, 4), ($^-2$, $^-3$), ($^-2$, 8), ($^-2$, $^-5$), ($^-2$, $^-7$)

b (3, 3), ($^-3$, $^-3$), (5, 5), (0, 0), ($^-2$, $^-2$)

c (2, 6), (3, 9), (1, 3), (0, 0), (5, 15)

d (1, 7), (2, 12), (3, 17), (4, 22), (10, 52)

13A Symmetry

Example

How many lines of symmetry does this shape have?

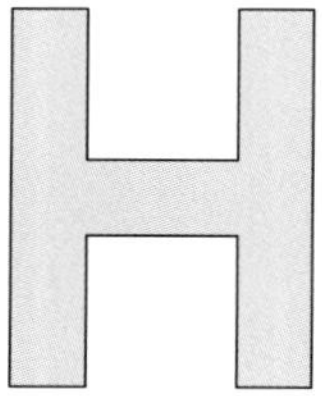

The shape has two lines of symmetry.

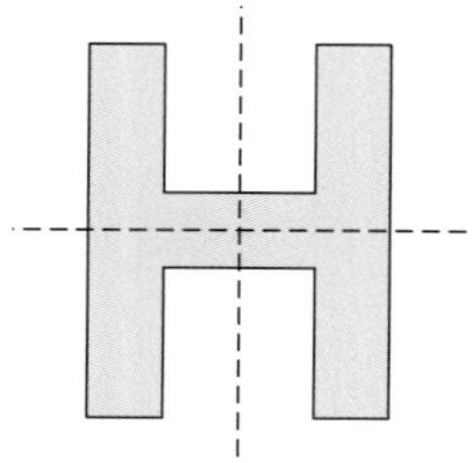

Copy the shapes and mark all the lines of symmetry.
How many lines of symmetry does each shape have?

1

2

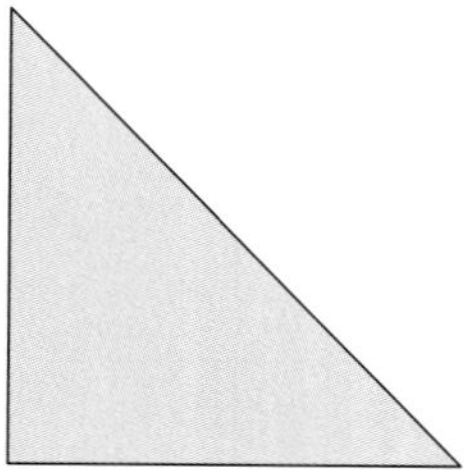

3

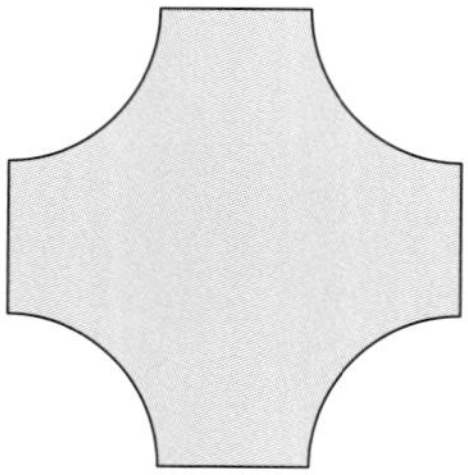

4

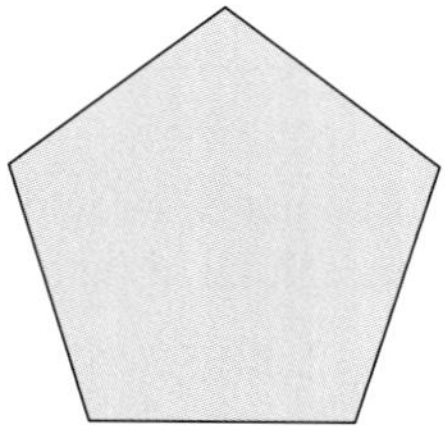

5

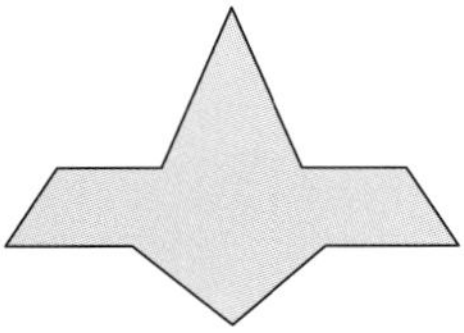

6

7

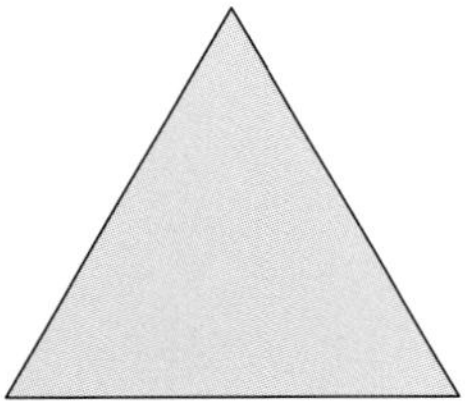

8

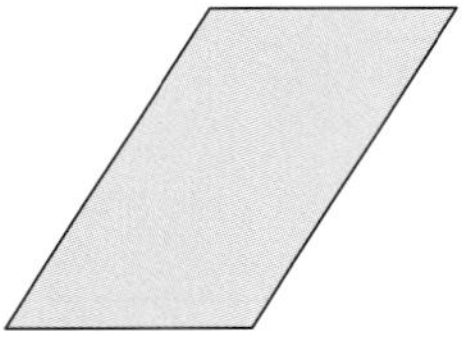

9

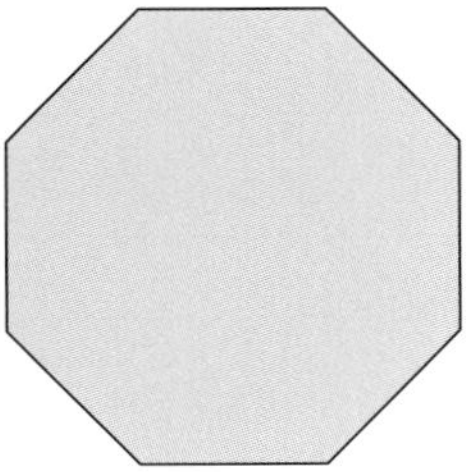

10

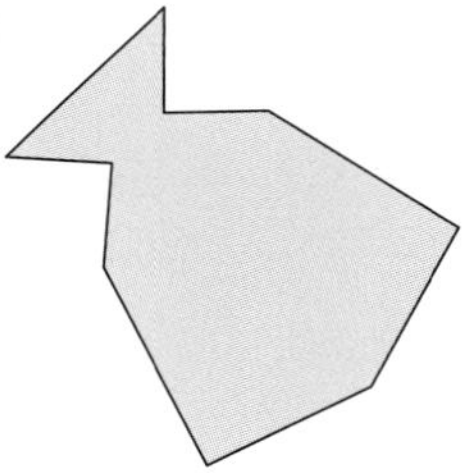

11

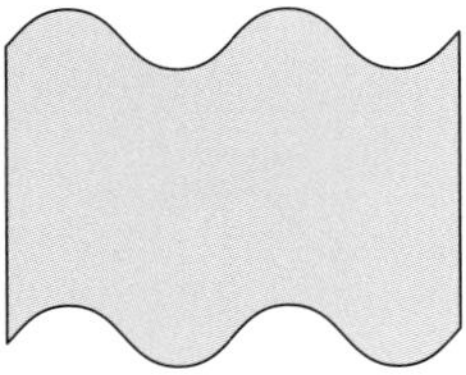

12

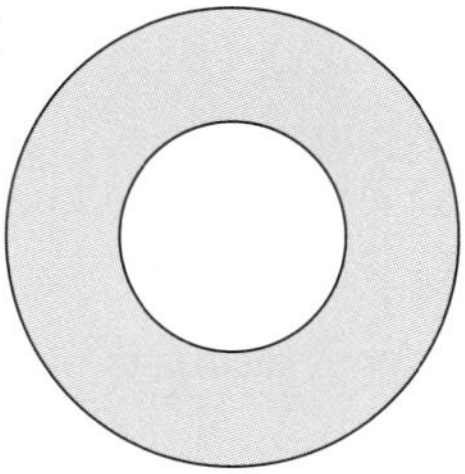

13B Reflection

Example

Reflect this shape in the mirror line.

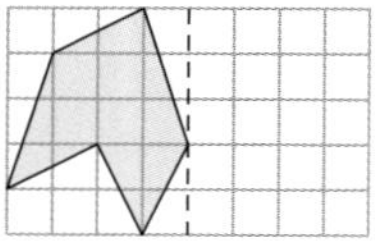

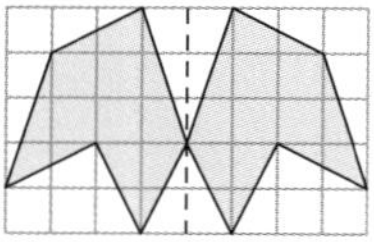

1 Copy each diagram and reflect each shape in the mirror line.

a

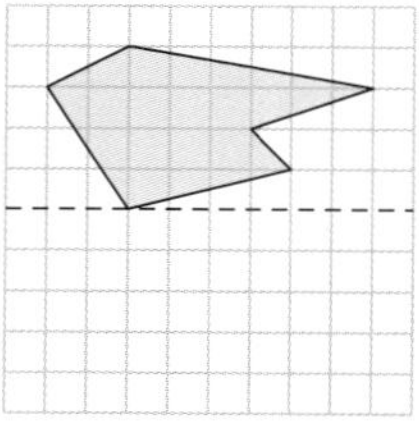

b

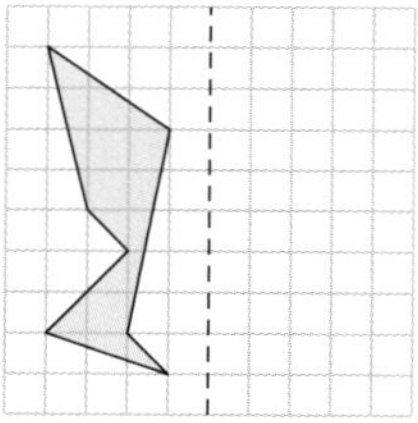

c

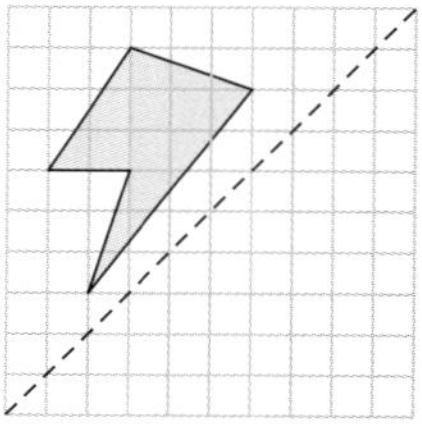

2 **a** Copy this diagram.
Reflect the shape first in the line X and then in the line Y.

b Copy the diagram again.
Reflect the shape first in the line Y and then in the line X.

c Comment on your results to parts **a** and **b**.

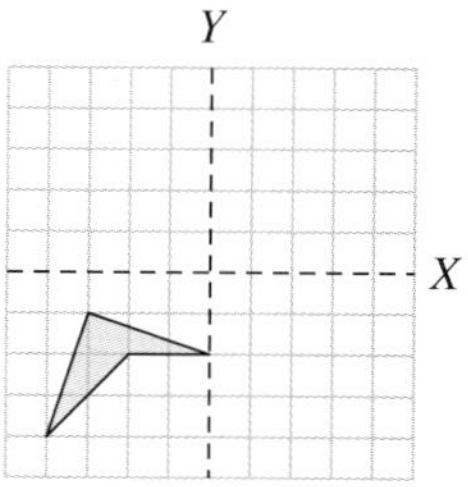

3 Copy and complete these diagrams by reflecting the shaded squares repeatedly in both mirror lines.
(Your final diagrams should have two lines of symmetry.)

a

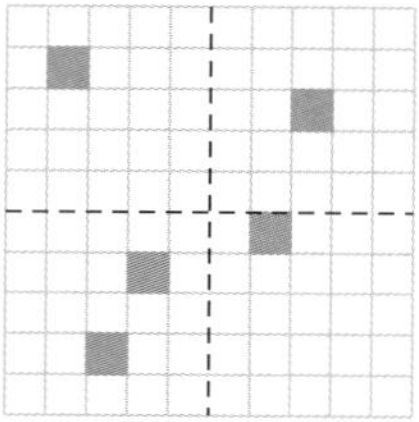

b

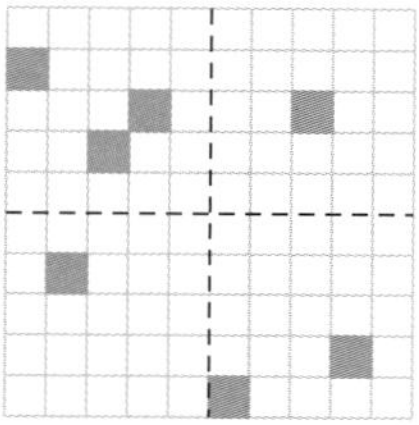

c

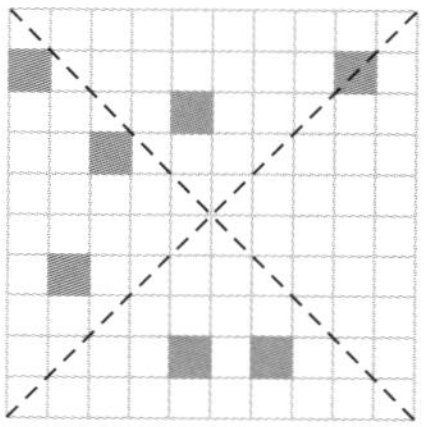

4 Draw a grid with the x-axis from $^{-}6$ to 6 and the y-axis from $^{-}6$ to 6.
Draw a pentagon ABCDE with vertices:
A = (2, 0) B = (5, 3) C = (0, 6) D = ($^{-}3$, 5) E = ($^{-}6$, 1)

a Reflect this pentagon in the x-axis.

b Is your image congruent to pentagon ABCDE? Give reasons for your answer.

5 Reflecting the pattern in the lines made this kaleidoscope pattern.
Make a kaleidoscope pattern of your own.

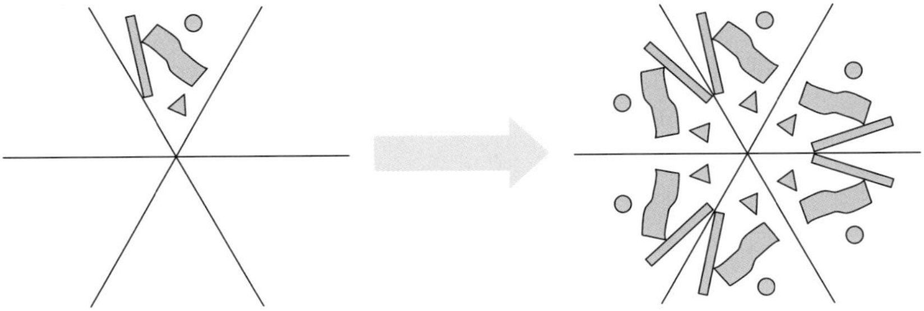

13C–13D Translation

Example

Describe the translation that takes:

a shape A to shape B

b shape B to shape C

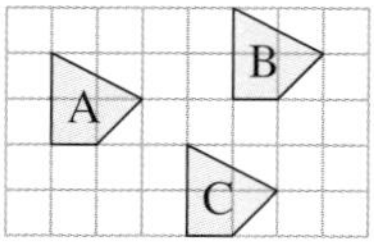

a A to B is a translation of 4 right and 1 up.

b B to C is a translation of 1 left and 3 down.

1 Describe these translations.

a A to B **b** A to C **c** A to E

d A to D **e** D to A **f** E to B

g E to A **h** C to D **i** D to B

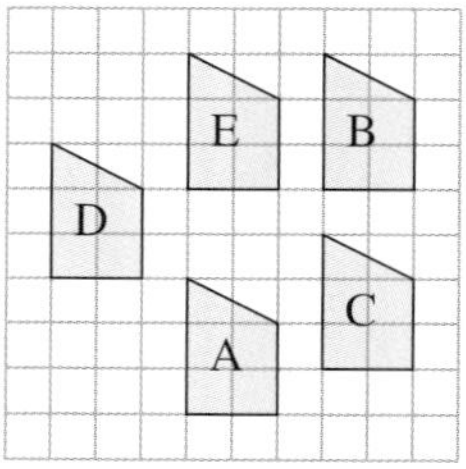

2 Describe these translations.

a A to B **b** A to C **c** A to E

d A to D **e** D to A **f** E to B

g E to A **h** C to D **i** D to B

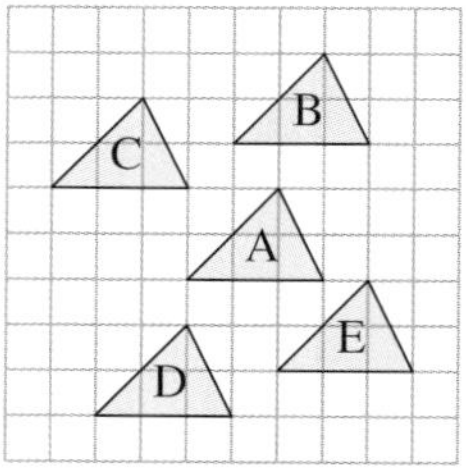

3 Copy this diagram and draw the image of the shape after each of these translations.

a 2 right, 1 up **b** 1 right, 3 down

c 4 left, 0 up **d** 3 left, 3 up

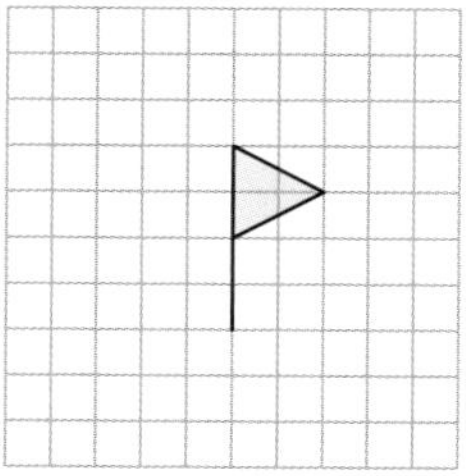

4 The point P has coordinates $(3, ^{-}2)$. The point P is translated 2 left and 5 down. What are the new coordinates?

5 Describe the translation that maps:

a (5, 1) onto (3, 7)

b (3, $^{-}4$) onto ($^{-}5$, 8)

6 Draw a pair of axes from 0 to 10.

a Draw a triangle with vertices (1, 1), (3, 1) and (3, 4).
Label this triangle A.

b Translate triangle A 6 right and 2 up. Label this image B.

c Translate triangle B 3 left and 3 up. Label this image C.

d Describe the translation that would take triangle A directly onto triangle C.

7 These are the coordinates of three of the vertices of a parallelogram ABCD:

A = (5, 4) B = ($^{-}3$, 5) C = ($^{-}6$, 1)

The parallelogram is translated 4 right and 3 down, to the image A'B'C'D'.
What are the coordinates of D', the image of the fourth vertex?

13E–13F Rotation and rotational symmetry

Example

State the order of rotational symmetry of this shape.

The shape will fit onto itself twice in one whole turn.
So the shape has rotational symmetry of order 2.

1 Find the order of rotational symmetry of each shape.

a

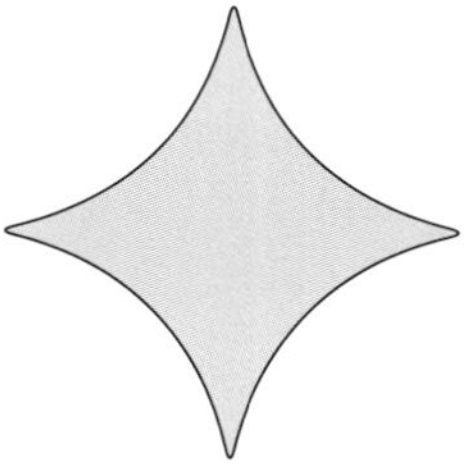

b

c

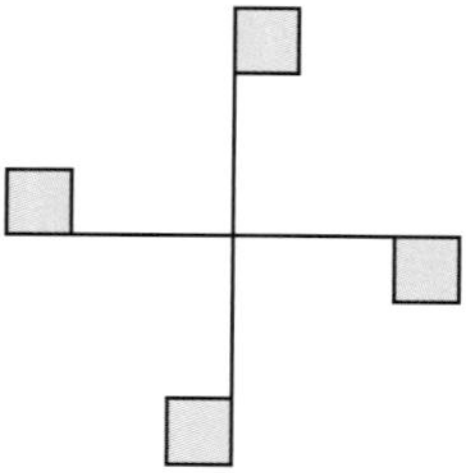

d

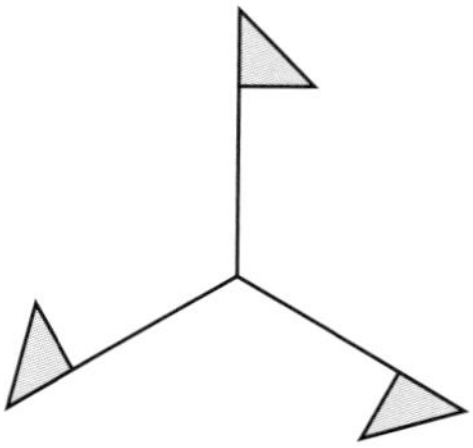

e

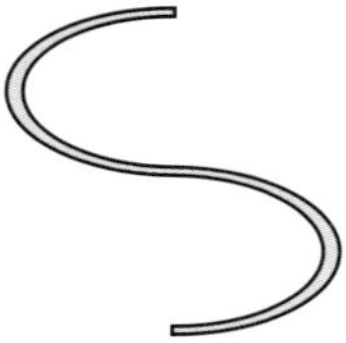

f

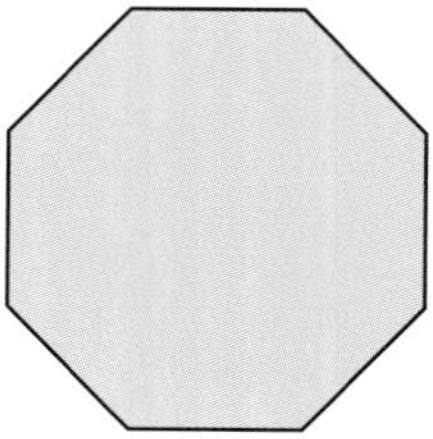

g

h

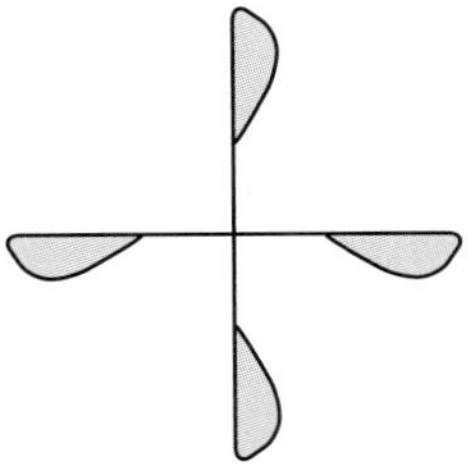

i

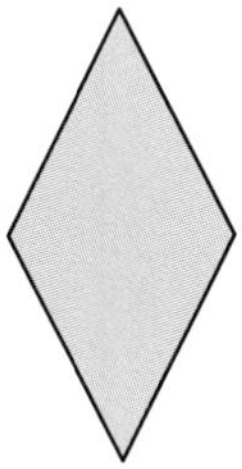

j

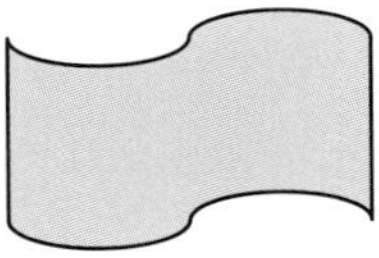

k

l

2 Find the number of lines of symmetry for each of the shapes in question **1**.

13G Rotation about a given point

Example

Rotate this shape 180° about the black dot.

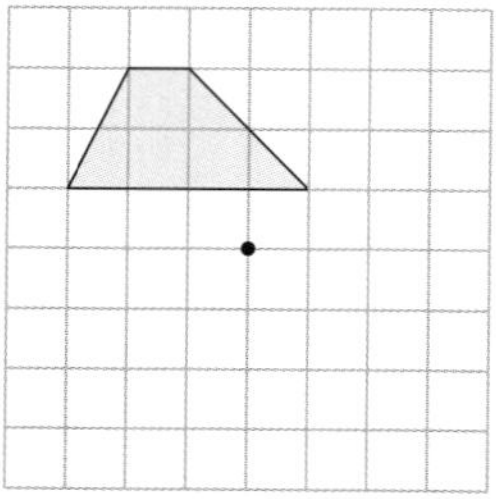

A rotation of 180° can be either clockwise or anticlockwise.

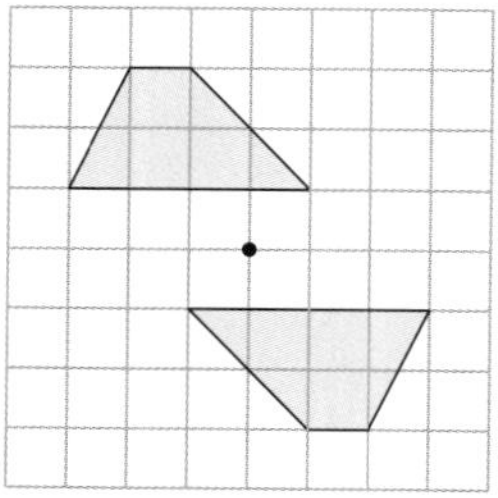

1 Copy the diagrams and rotate each shape about the black dot by the angle given.

a

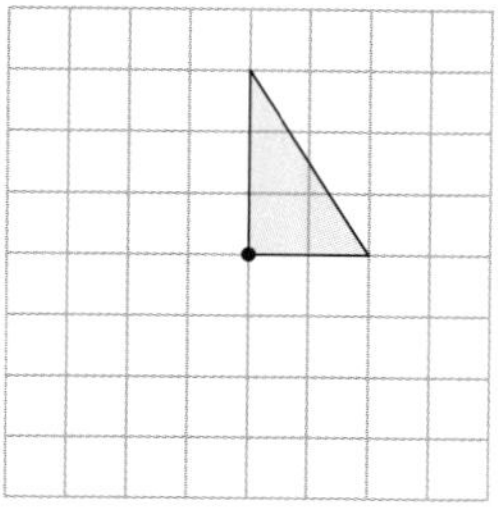

90° clockwise

b

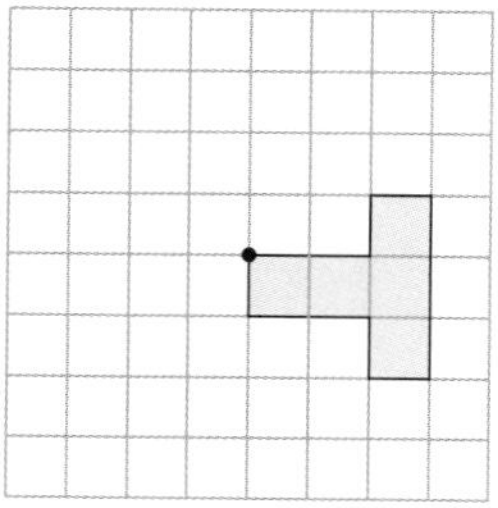

180°

c

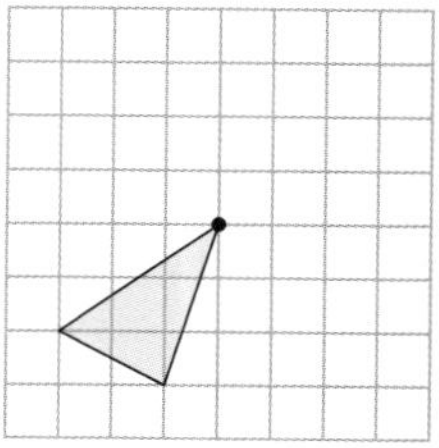

90° anticlockwise

d

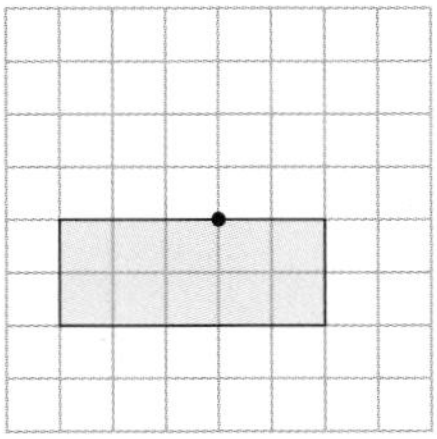

180°

e

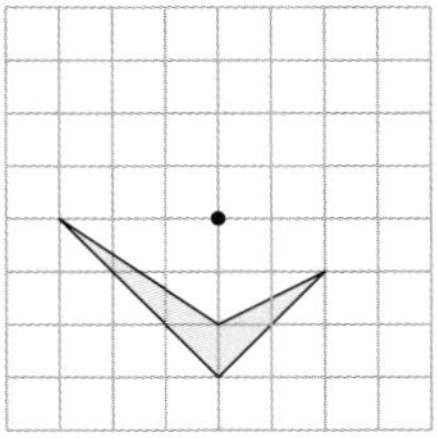

180°

f

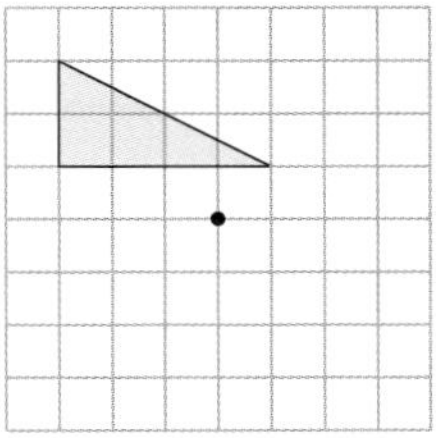

90° clockwise

g

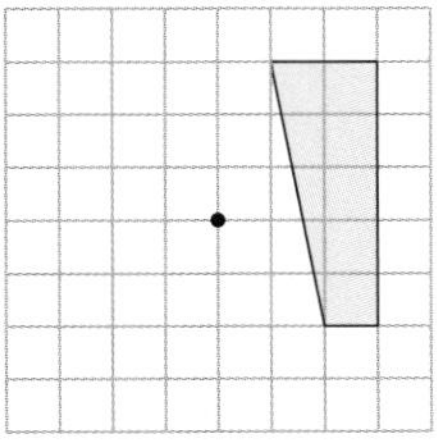

180°

h

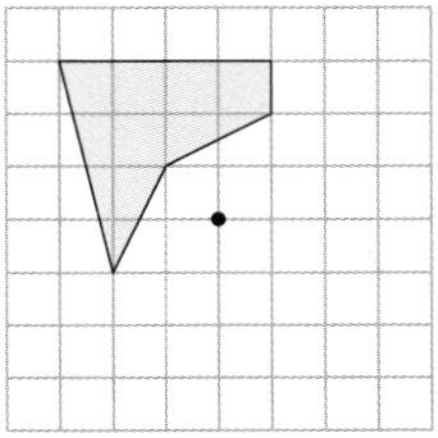

270° clockwise

i

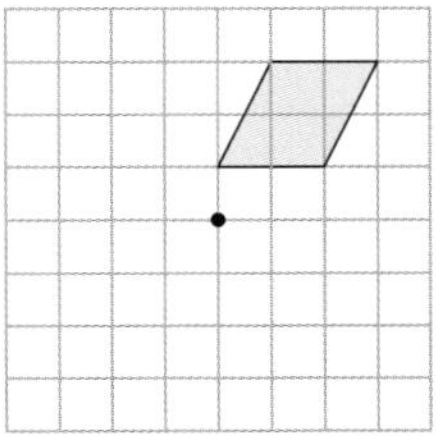

270° anticlockwise

2 Draw triangle ABC with vertices at (1, 0), (1, 3) and (3, 0).
Rotate triangle ABC 90° anticlockwise about the point (0, $^{-}1$).

3 Describe the rotation that maps shape A onto shape B.

a

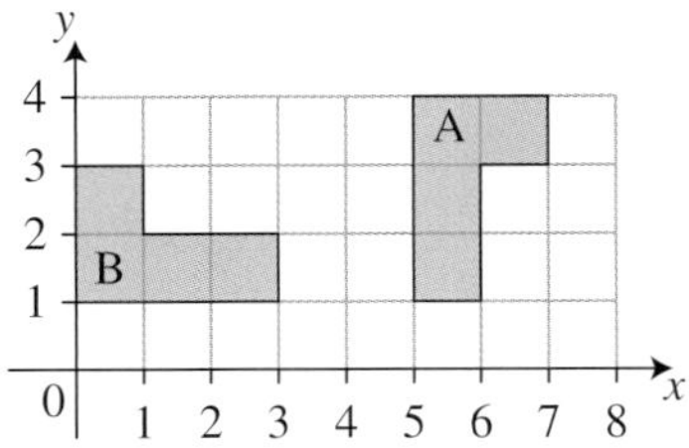

b

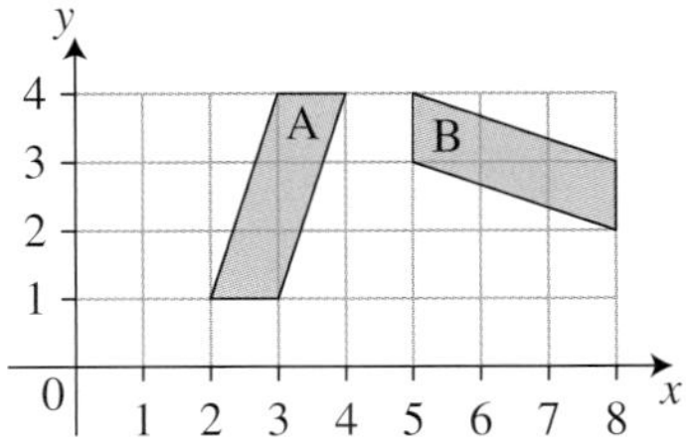

4 **a** The points (4, 0), (0, 5), (4, 2) and ($^{-}3$, 4) are each rotated 90° anticlockwise about the origin.

i Copy and complete the table.

Point	(4, 0)	(0, 5)	(4, 2)	($^{-}3$, 4)
Image	(0, 4)			

ii Describe in words a rule for writing down the image of any point after a rotation of 90° anticlockwise about the origin.

b Find a rule for writing down the image of a point after a rotation of 180° about the origin.

c Find a rule for writing down the image of a point after a rotation of 90° clockwise about the origin.

13H Enlargement

Example

Enlarge the shape by a scale factor of 2, using the point shown as the centre of enlargement.

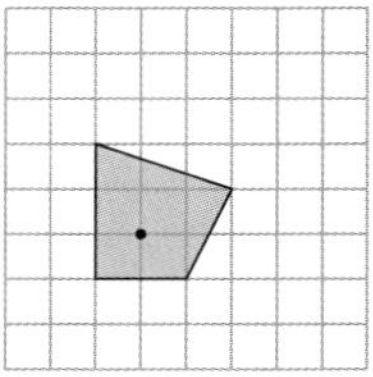

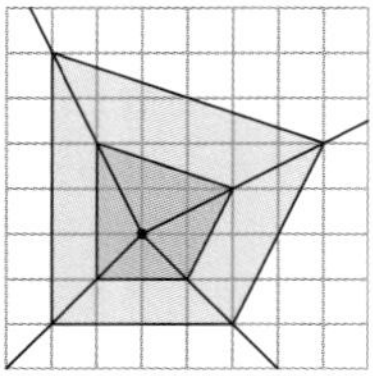

1 Write down the scale factor for each enlargement.

a

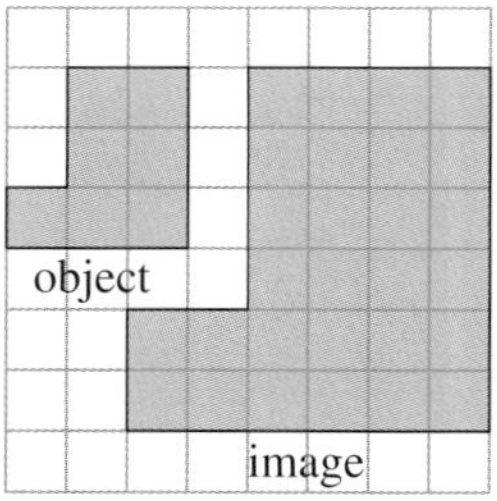

b

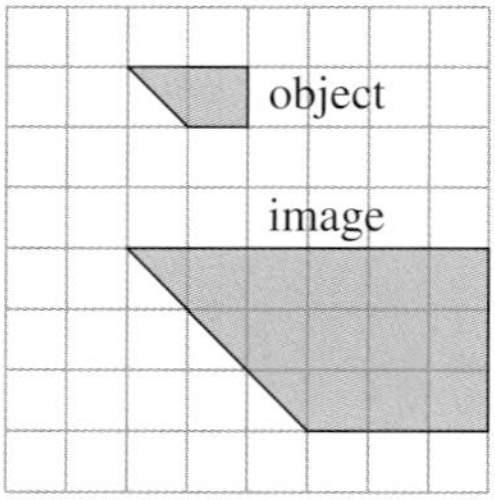

2 Copy these shapes on squared paper.
Using the centre O, enlarge the shapes by the scale factor shown.

a Scale factor 2

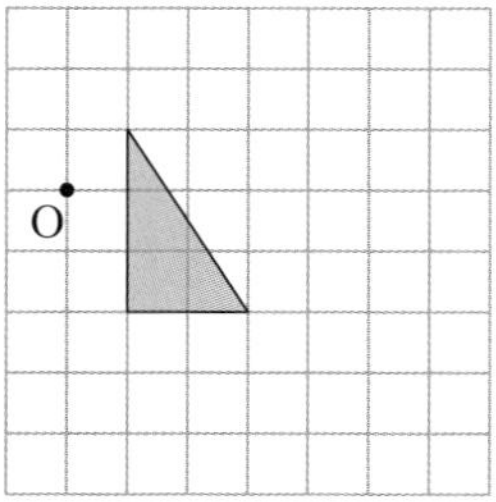

b Scale factor 3

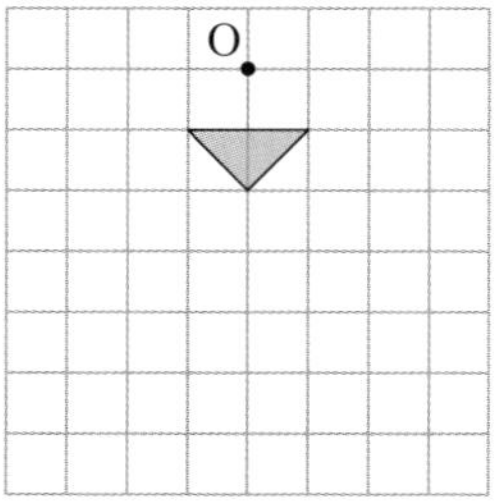

c Scale factor 2

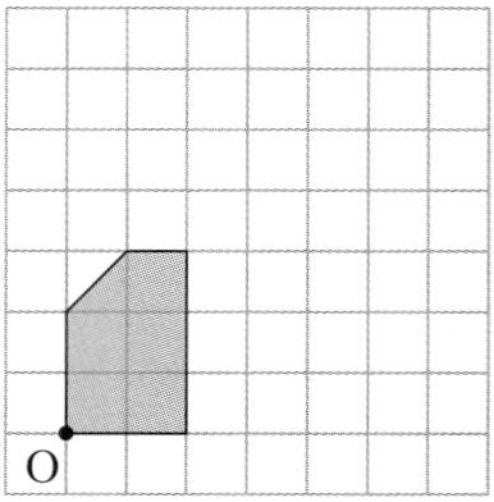

3 Draw a shape of your own on squared paper.
Choose a point to use as the centre of enlargement and enlarge your shape by a scale factor of 4.

13I–13J Scale drawing

Example

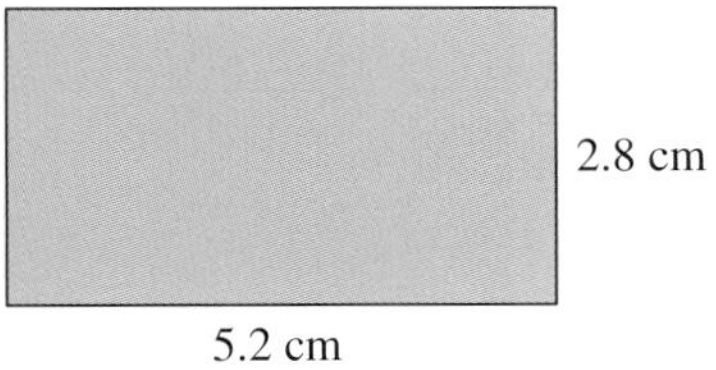

The diagram shows the plan of a garden.
The plan has been drawn using a scale of 1 cm to 5 m.
What are the actual dimensions of the garden?

1 cm represents 5 m,
so 5.2 cm represents $5.2 \times 5 = 26$ m
and 2.8 cm represents $2.8 \times 5 = 14$ m
The garden is 26 m by 14 m.

1 Copy and complete this table.

	Length on map	Scale	Actual length
a	5 cm	1 cm represents 2 m	
b	2.5 cm	1 cm represents 5 km	
c		1 cm represents 20 m	160 m
d	12 cm		48 km
e	8.4 cm	1 cm represents 10 m	
f		1 cm represents 50 km	260 km
g	7.5 cm		300 m

2 Write these scales in ratio form.

a 1 cm represents 8 m **b** 1 cm represents 5 km **c** 1 cm represents 0.5 km

d 1 cm represents 2.5 m **e** 1 mm represents 5 cm **f** 1 mm represents 2 km

3 Find the actual length and width of these rectangles if they have been drawn to a scale of:

i 1 : 20 **ii** 1 : 500 **iii** 1 : 40 000

a

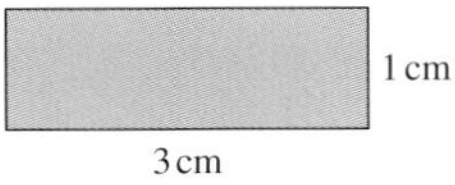

b

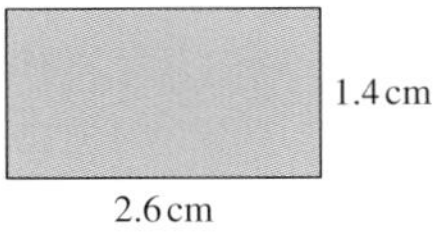

14A Language of probability

Example

Give an example of:

a an impossible event **b** a certain event.

a Impossible event: picking a letter F from the word RHOMBUS.

b Certain event: picking a square number from the set {4, 9, 16, 25}.

1 Copy this probability scale and arrange the cards at the correct points on the scale.

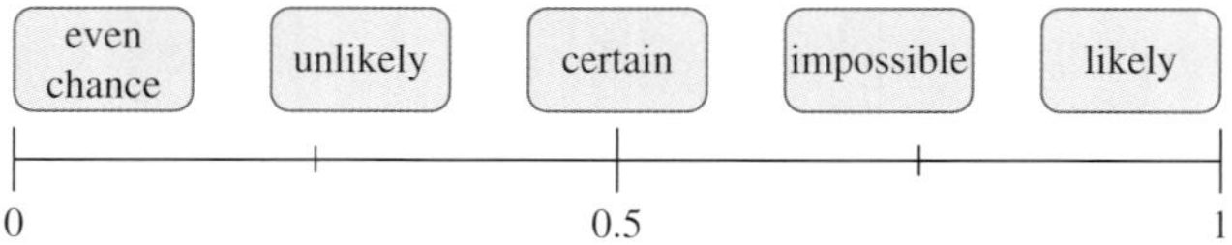

2 Make a copy of the probability scale from question **1**. Place an arrow and the letter of each event in the list below at the correct point on your scale.

a If you pick a ball from a bag containing only red balls, you will get a red ball.

b If you toss a coin you will get a 'head'.

c If you throw a dice you will get a 5.

d Your Maths teacher is 15 years old.

e If you toss two coins, you will get at least one tail.

3 Assign a probability of 0 or 1 to each event.

a You will blink in the next hour.

b You will run 30 km in the next hour.

c If you throw a dice you will get a number smaller than 7.

d If you pick a ball from a bag containing three green balls, you will pick a pink ball.

e If you pick a letter from the word SPY you will pick a vowel.

4 Today is Tuesday. What is the probability that tomorrow will be Wednesday? Write your answer as a percentage.

5 Write your answers as fractions in this question.
Jessie picks a number at random from the set {1, 2, 3, 4, 5, 6, 7, 8}.
What is the probability that she picks:

a an even number **b** a number less than 8

c a square number **d** a prime number?

14B Experimental probability

Example

A tin is picked at random from a box containing 100 tins.
65 of the tins have labels and 35 do not have labels.
What is the of probability of picking

a a tin with a label **b** a tin without a label?

a $P(\text{label}) = \frac{65}{100} = \frac{13}{20}$ **b** $P(\text{no label}) = \frac{35}{100} = \frac{7}{20}$

1 An ordinary six-sided dice is thrown 60 times.
The results are shown in the table.

Score	1	2	3	4	5	6
Frequency	7	20	8	9	8	8

a What fraction of the 60 throws result in:

i a 2 **ii** a 4 **iii** a 5

iv a 0 **v** an even number **vi** an odd number

vii a prime number **viii** a score of 5 or less?

b Do you think the dice is fair? Explain your answer.

2 The marks for 50 students in a test are shown in the table.

Marks	1	2	3	4	5	6	7	8	9	10
Frequency	2	3	5	5	7	8	10	4	3	3

What is the probability that a student chosen at random scored:

a 7 marks **b** 9 marks **c** 3 marks

d more than 6 marks **e** 3 marks or more **f** less than 4 marks?

3 Jarred has red pencils and blue pencils in his pencil case. He selects a pencil at random, records its colour and replaces the pencil in the pencil case. He repeats this 50 times. The results are shown.

Red	35
Blue	15

a Estimate the probability that the next pencil Jarred selects is
i red **ii** blue.

b How can Jarred improve his probability estimates?

14C Theoretical probability

Example

A bag contains 3 red, 2 blue and 5 green marbles.
A marble is picked out of the bag at random.
Find the probability that the marble is:

a red **b** blue **c** green

(Note: there are $3 + 2 + 5 = 10$ marbles to choose from.)

a $P(\text{red}) = \frac{3}{10}$ **b** $P(\text{blue}) = \frac{2}{10} = \frac{1}{5}$

c $P(\text{green}) = \frac{5}{10} = \frac{1}{2}$

1 A bag contains 5 black and 2 white balls.
A ball is picked out of the bag at random.
Find the probability that it is:

a black **b** white **c** green

2 One of these five cards is chosen at random.

[2] [3] [5] [7] [8]

Find the probability of choosing a card with a number that is:

a a 3 **b** a 5 **c** an odd number

d an even number **e** a prime number **f** a factor of 24

g greater than 10 **h** less than 10 **i** a factor of 280

3 [P] [A] [R] [A] [L] [L] [E] [L] [O] [G] [R] [A] [M]

One of these 13 cards is chosen at random.
Find the probability of choosing a card with a letter that is:

a a G **b** an A

c an R **d** not an E

e not an L **f** a vowel

g also from the word LARGE

4

Colour	Red	Blue	Green
Probability	$\frac{1}{2}$	$\frac{1}{3}$	$\frac{1}{6}$

A circular spinner has a red, a blue and a green section. This table shows the probabilities of the spinner landing on each of the three sections. Draw the spinner.

15A Real-life graphs

Example

This graph shows the cost of lengths of ribbon.

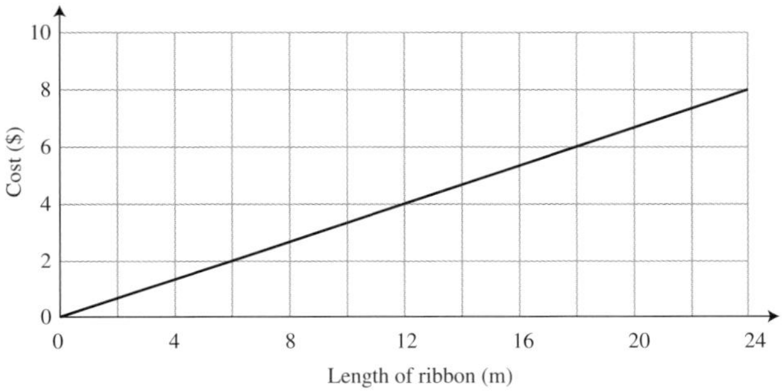

a How much does 6 m of ribbon cost?
b How many metres of ribbon can you buy for $1?
c How much ribbon can be bought for $40?

---

a 6 m of ribbon costs $2.
b 3 m of ribbon can be bought for $1.
c $40 \times 3 = 120$
So 120 m of ribbon can be bought for $40.

1 This graph shows the cost of a taxi for different distances.

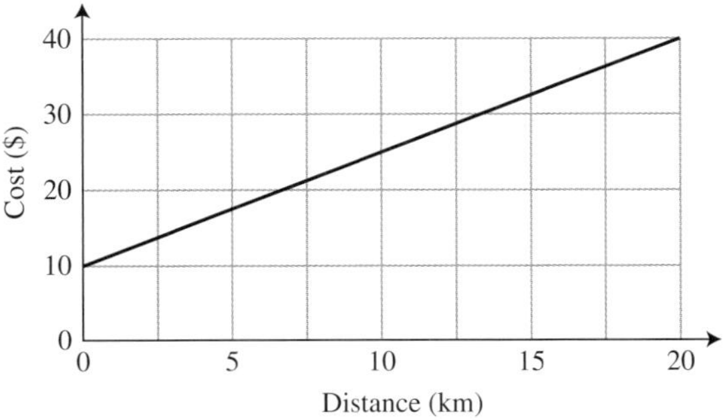

For each journey there is a fixed charge plus a charge for the distance.

a What is the cost of a 10 km journey?

b How much is the fixed charge?

c Estimate the cost of a 40 km journey.

2 This graph shows the temperature at a place on 27th February.

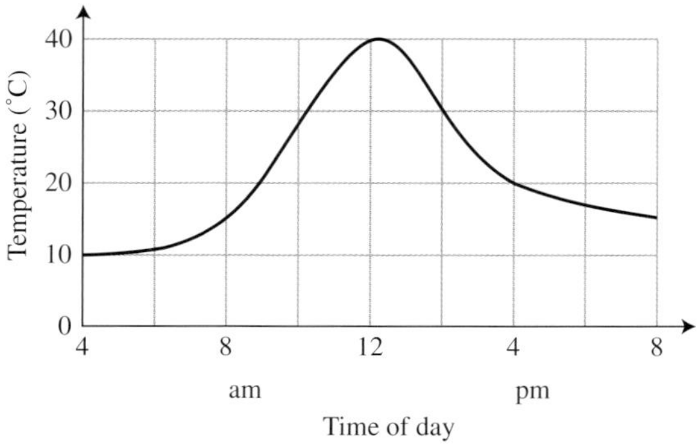

a What was the temperature at 8 am?

b What was the temperature at 3 pm?

c When was the temperature 20°C?

3 Tara makes a cup of tea and leaves it to cool. She records its temperature every ten minutes. Her results are shown in this table.

Time (minutes)	0	10	20	30	40	50	60
Temperature (°C)	100	70	55	47	42	38	36

Draw a graph to show this information.
Use your graph to estimate the time at which the temperature of the tea was 60°C.

15B Travel graphs

Example

Parminder leaves home at 2 pm to go on a bike ride.
She stops once for a rest.
The travel graph shows information about her journey.

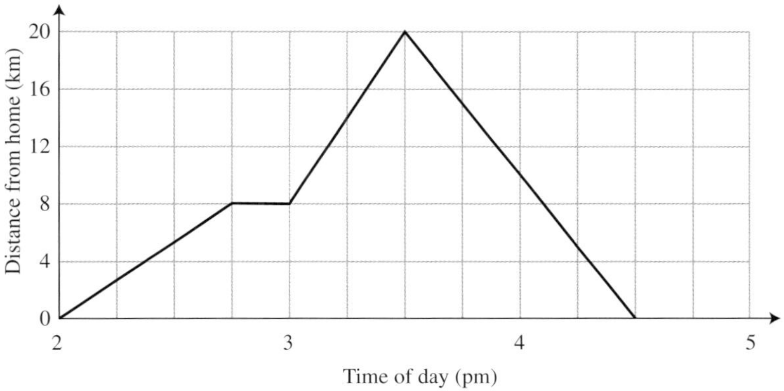

a For how long does Parminder stop for a rest?

b At what time does she arrive back home?

c Between which times was she travelling fastest?

d How far does she travel in total?

e Calculate her average speed, in km/h, for the last hour of her journey.

f Calculate her average speed, in km/h, for the whole journey.

---

a She stops from 2:45 pm to 3 pm = 15 minutes.

b She arrives back home at 4:30 pm.

c She travels fastest when the graph is steepest.
This is between 3 pm and 3:30 pm.

d Total distance travelled = $20 + 20 = 40\,\text{km}$

e Average speed for last hour of journey $= \dfrac{\text{distance travelled}}{\text{time taken}}$

$$= \frac{20}{1} = 20\,\text{km/h}$$

f Average speed for whole journey $= \dfrac{\text{total distance travelled}}{\text{time taken}}$

$$= \frac{20 + 20}{2.5} = 16\,\text{km/h}$$

1 Here is the distance–time graph for a bus journey.

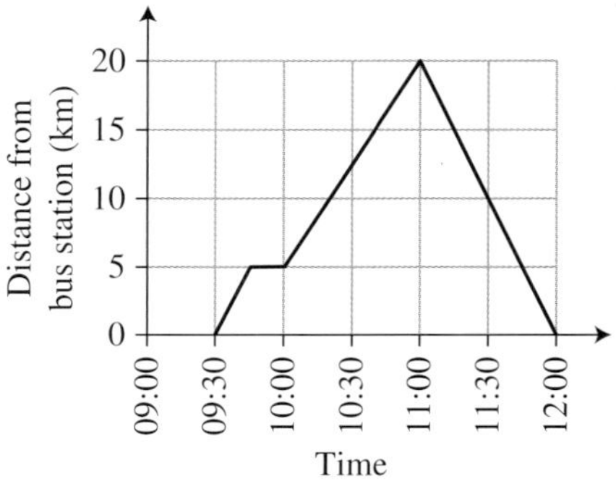

a Find, in kilometres per hour, the average speed of the bus:

i between 10:00 and 11:00

ii between 11:00 and 12:00

b Between which times is the bus stationary?

2 Zelda swims in a 100 m race. The swimming pool is 50 m long. She swims the first length in 35 seconds and the second length in 40 seconds.

a Draw a travel graph to show this information.

b Calculate her average speed, in m/s, for the first length.

c Calculate her average speed, in m/s, for the second length.

d Calculate her average speed, in m/s, for the entire race.

16A–16B Sets

Example

List the members of these sets.

a {factors of 36}

b {prime numbers between 70 and 80}

---

a {factors of 36} = {1, 2, 3, 4, 6, 9, 12, 18, 36}

b {prime numbers between 70 and 80} = {71, 73, 79}

1 List the members of these sets.

a {factors of 45}

b {even numbers between 31 and 41}

c {prime numbers between 20 and 30}

d {square numbers less than 30}

e {odd numbers between 70 and 90}

2 Write down two more members of each of these sets.

a {a, b, c, d, e, …}

b $\{+, \div, \sqrt{\ }, \ldots\}$

c {red, orange, yellow, …}

d {1, 4, 9, 16, …}

e {triangle, quadrilateral, pentagon, …}

3 Describe these sets in words.

a {Saturday, Sunday}

b {w, x, y, z}

c {1, 2, 3, 4, 6, 12}

d {spring, summer, autumn, winter}

4 Describe these sets in words.

a

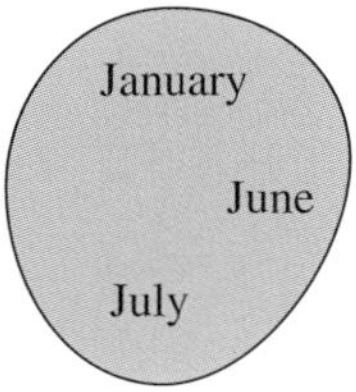

b

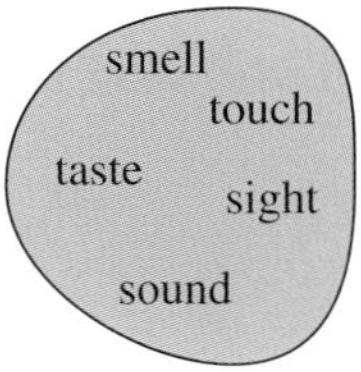

c

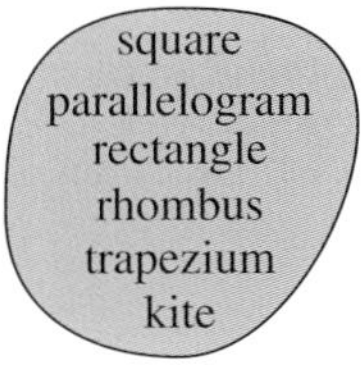

16C Describing sets with symbols

Example

Are these statements true or false?

a 49 □ {square numbers}

b pentagon ∈ {polygons}

c {countries south of the equator} = ∅

---

a FALSE (49 is a square number because $7 \times 7 = 49$)

b TRUE (a pentagon is a five-sided polygon)

c FALSE (Australia, for example, is a country that is south of the equator.)

1 Are these statements true or false?

a 27 ∈ {9, 18, 27, 36}

b 6 ∈ {even numbers}

c elephant ∈ {animals with two legs}

d triangle ∈ {polygons}

e Jupiter □ {planets}

f 5 □ {odd numbers}

g 1 □ {prime numbers}

h 7 □ {factors of 20}

i 3 □ {2, 4, 6, 8, 10}

2 Which of these sets are empty and which are not empty?

a {months of the year with 32 days}

b {even prime numbers}

c {prime numbers between 48 and 52}

d {triangles with two right angles}

e {quadrilaterals with two obtuse angles}

f {months of the year beginning with the letter M}

g {prime numbers between 78 and 88}

h {countries north of the north pole}

i {hexagons with two right angles}

j {obtuse angles that are smaller than 100°}

k {elephants that can fly}

16D–16E Venn diagrams

Example

Show {4, 9}   {1, 4, 9, 16, 25} on a Venn diagram.

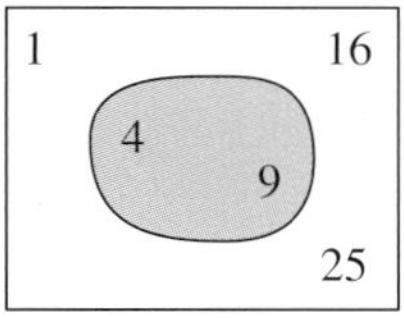

1 numbers between 0 and 11

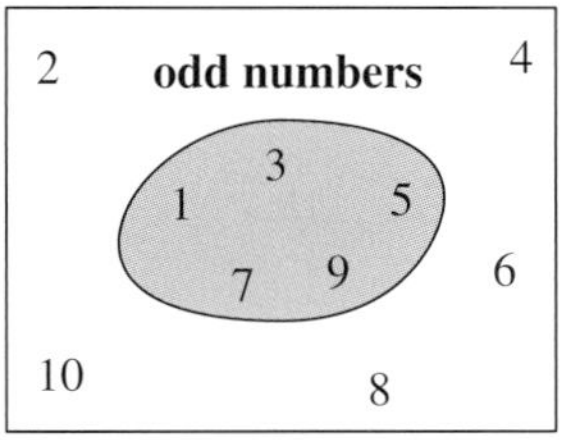

a List the members of the universal set.

b List the members of the subset.

2 Which of these statements are true and which are false?

a {1, 2, 3}   {1, 2, 3, 4, 5}

b {a, b, c}   {b, c}

c {4, 7}   {4, 8, 12, 16}

d {2, 4}   {even numbers}

e {1, 2, 3}   {prime numbers}

f {Tuesday}   {months of the year}

g {factors of 15}   {1, 2, 3, 4, 5, 6, 7, 8, 9, 10}

3 Show each of these on a Venn diagram.

a {a, b, c}   {a, b, c, d, e, f, g}

b {2, 5, 8, 11}   {1, 2, 3, 4, 5, 6, 7, 8, 9, 10, 11, 12}

c {red, orange, green}   {red, orange, yellow, green, blue}

d {□, △} ⊂ {○, □, ▭, △, ▱}

e 

f 

16F Intersection of sets

Example

The universal set = {1, 2, 3, 4, 5, 6}
A = {odd numbers}
B = {prime numbers}
Show the universal set and the subsets A and B on a Venn diagram.

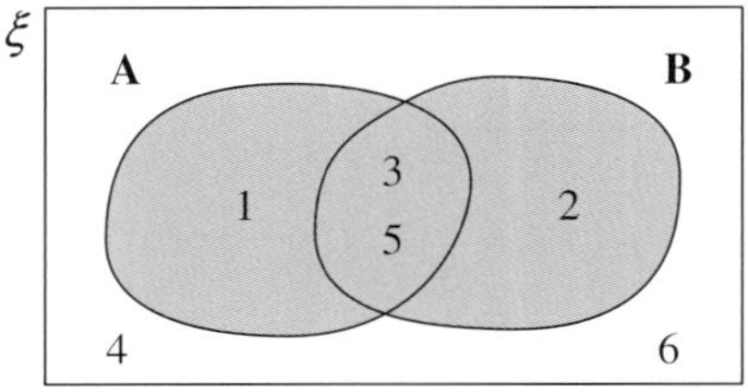

1

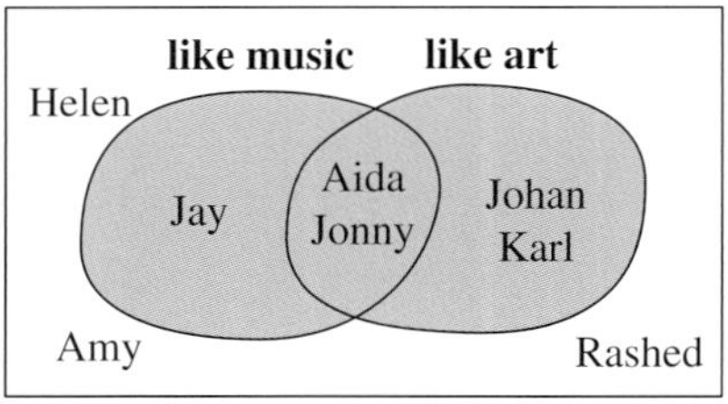

This Venn diagram shows information about eight students in Form 1A.
List the subset of students who:

a like music
b like art
c like both music and art
d do not like art
e do not like music
f like music but not art
g like art but not music
h do not like music and do not like art.

2

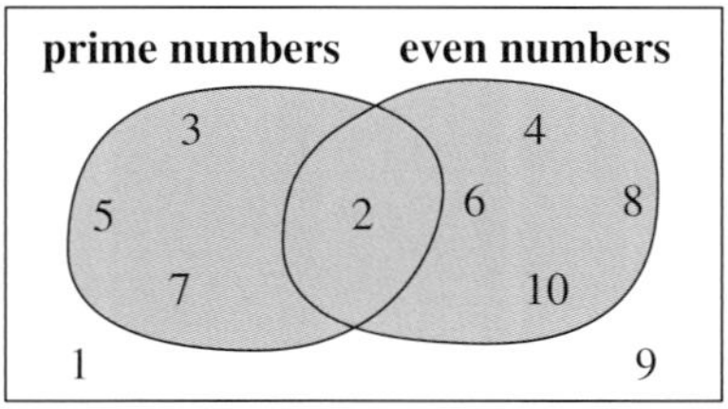

This Venn diagram shows information about the whole numbers from 1 to 10.
List the subset of numbers that are:

a prime
b even
c even and prime
d not prime
e not prime and even
f not prime and not even.

16G–16H Common factors

Example

Use a Venn diagram to find:

a the common factors of 16 and 20

b the HCF of 16 and 20

factors of 16 = {1, 2, 4, 8, 16}

factors of 20 = {1, 2, 4, 5, 10, 20}

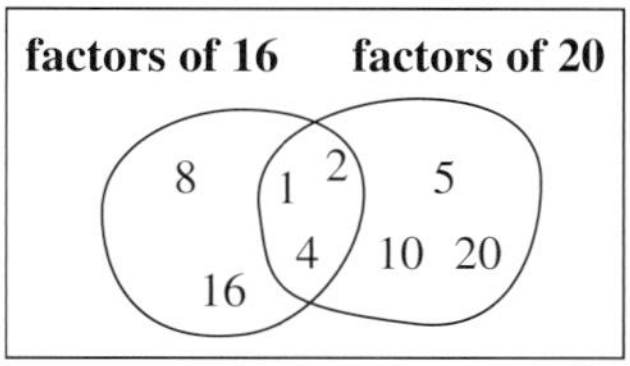

a Common factors of 16 and 20 = {1, 2, 4}

b The HCF of 16 and 20 is 4.

1 **a** Write down the set of factors of 6.

b Write down the set of factors of 12.

c Copy and complete this Venn diagram.

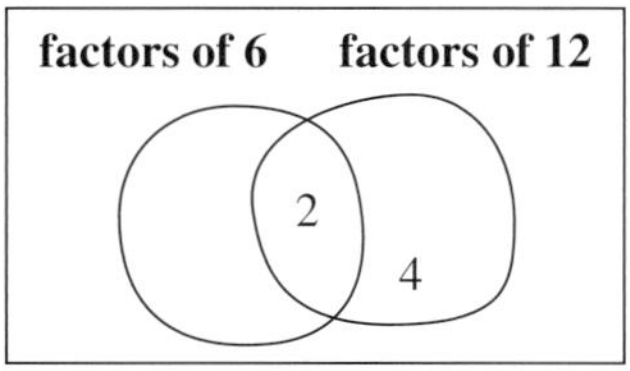

d Write down the set of common factors of 6 and 12.

e Write down the HCF of 6 and 12.

2 For each of the following pairs of numbers, use a Venn diagram to find:

i the common factors **ii** the HCF

a 15 and 18 **b** 10 and 12 **c** 14 and 42

d 24 and 56 **e** 42 and 51 **f** 34 and 85

3 **a** Write down the set of factors of:

i 18 **ii** 45 **iii** 30

b Copy and complete this Venn diagram.

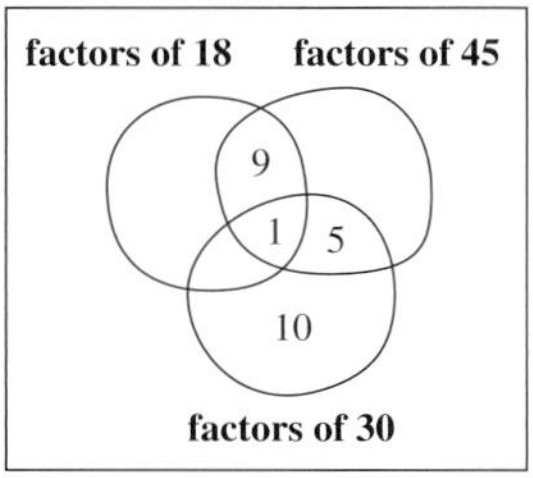

16I–16J Common multiples

Example

Show the first six multiples of 10 and the first four multiples of 15 on a Venn diagram.
Find the LCM of 10 and 15.

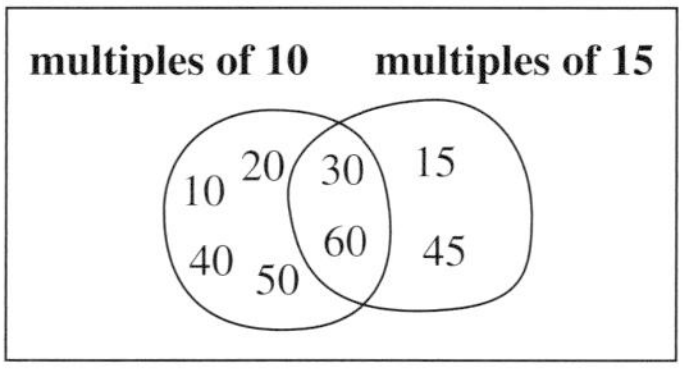

Common multiples of 10 and 15 = {30, 60}
So the LCM of 10 and 15 is 30.

1 **a** Write down the first ten multiples of 2.
b Write down the first four multiples of 5.
c Using your numbers from parts **a** and **b**, copy and complete this Venn diagram.

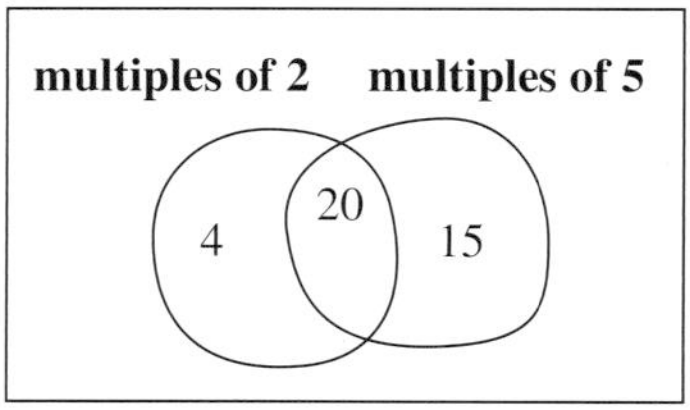

d Write down the LCM of 2 and 5.

2 **a** Write down the first twelve multiples of 3.
b Write down the first four multiples of 9.
c Using your numbers from parts **a** and **b**, copy and complete this Venn diagram.

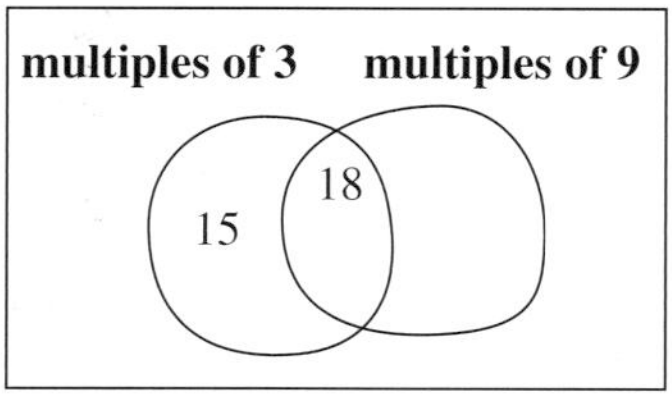

d Write down the LCM of 3 and 9.

3 Use a Venn diagram to find the LCM of each of these pairs of numbers.

a 2 and 10 **b** 5 and 2 **c** 9 and 4
d 6 and 8 **e** 5 and 6 **f** 4 and 7
g 4 and 10 **h** 6 and 10 **i** 9 and 6